CW00765624

Graham Maclachlan

THE
GREEN
ALMANAC

LOCHAR PUBLISHING · MOFFAT · SCOTLAND

© Graham Maclachlan, 1991

Published by Lochar Publishing Ltd
Moffat DG10 9ED

British Library Cataloguing in Publication Data
Maclachlan, Graham
    The green almanac.
    1. Environment
    I. Title
    333.7

ISBN 0–948403–72–1

Typeset in $8\frac{1}{2}$ on $9\frac{1}{2}$pt Garamond 49 by
Chapterhouse, Formby
Printed in Scotland
by Eagle Colourbooks

For Duncan and Douglas

Publisher's Note

The author and publisher would like to thank the following individuals and organisations for providing illustrations:

Howden Turbines, Oxford Environmental Films, British Petroleum Solar, Chris K. Mylne, Animal Aid, Ecover – Full Moon, Government of Australia, Nick Price, Jane Anderson, Our Common Inheritance – David Darling, Alan Wilson, London Transport, G. Magnin – ICPB, Scottish Power, Pilkington Insulation, British Plastics Federation, Safeways, United Glass, British National Anti-Vivisection Society, International Whaling Commission, ASH Scotland, David Roberts, General Motors UK Ltd, Swedish Environmental Agency, Oates Associates, ABAL studies, Allan Stewart, Aluminium Can Recycling Association, Sue Cunningham Picture Library, J. Lovett World Wildlife Fund UK

Acknowledgments

I would like to thank the members of the Board of **Friends of the Earth** (Scotland) and my colleagues Xanthe Jay and Simon Lee for the encouragement and support. Thanks also to Mike Thornton of **LEEP** for his help, and especially to Sheena Phillips for keeping me on the right track and reading the manuscripts when she had other things on her mind and of course thanks to Beryl and Layla for doing the most difficult job of all, living with me.

All opinions, errors and ommisions expressed in the Green Almanac are mine alone and not the responsibility of any of the people above.

Introduction

The idea of a Green Almanac was not to produce a definitive study of every environmental problem on the planet, that would be impossible, but to 'snapshot' some of the major and many of the minor areas of concern. With a simple text outlining some of the key facts involved.

In compiling the book I have been awed by some of the statistics, for example, almost half of the women in the world are illiterate or that the Japanese throw away 2 billion chopsticks each year! It is estimated that there are only 500 blue whales left in Antarctic waters representing 0.2% of the estimated population prior to commercial whaling. This scale of devastation is still going on. One Italian environmental group estimate that each year 250 million birds are shot in that country for sport.

In making the choice of issues I have tried to show that people, animals and habitats are being destroyed at an unprecedented rate and that unless attention is drawn to them we will continue to lose the variety that makes our planet unique.

Around the world millions of indigenous people are being displaced and killed. To represent the type of horrors being committed I have included a section on the Yanomani and the Hupla Indians. Although these two groups of peoples live on the opposite sides of the globe and are numerically small their treatment is indicative of how native peoples are being treated by the 'civilised' world. Some of these small tribes are as rare as the white rhino yet very little is being done to protect them.

The common thread running through all the entries is that we can stop this destruction. In the What You Can Do section I have tried to show that no matter how remote the problem you can make a difference. The campaigning organistaions need your support.

By 'Acting Locally and Thinking Globally' we can all make changes for the better.

Contents

	Acknowledgments	3
	Introduction	4
1	Wildlife	6
2	Energy	19
3	Consumerism	34
4	Animal Welfare	69
5	World Resources	79
6	Water	104
7	Disasters	118
8	The Developing World	124
	Directory of Organisations	132
	Bibliography	144

1 Wildlife

Bat Populations Under Threat

LOCATION

British Isles

KEY FACTS

The number of bats in the British Isles is in serious decline, with at least one species now extinct and some others threatened, due mainly to loss of habitat and reduction of their food supply. Although now protected by law their roosts still get disturbed both accidentally and intentionally.

Structural alterations to buildings and the use of toxic chemicals to preserve roof timbers have both had a serious effect on the number of bats. The chemicals used in timber preservation are often persistent and may be lethal to bats which continue to use the roost many years after the initial treatment. The use of these organochlorine pesticides and pentachlorophenol fungicides are thought to have contributed to the 90% decline in the UK's horseshoe bat population.

The felling of mature trees and the general decline in native woodlands together with the increased use of pesticides, has meant a drop in the variety of insects available to bats and contributes to falling numbers.

It is an offence in Britain to intentionally disturb, damage or kill bats without consulting the Nature Conservancy Council.

WHAT CAN YOU DO

Try not to disturb bats either in caves or roofs. Put up a bat box

USEFUL CONTACTS

Nature Conservancy Council

The Bat Conservation Trust

Lothian Bat Group

Birds of Prey

LOCATION

United Kingdom

KEY FACTS

Following the widespread use of organochlorine pesticide like DDT after the Second World War the number of birds of prey, or raptors, in Europe and North America fell dramatically.

The birds, peregrine, merlin and sparrowhawk being the worst affected, were being slowly poisoned by the pesticide residues building up in the body fats of their prey causing loss of fertility and laying eggs with such thin shells that they broke before the young could hatch.

Numbers fell so low that in Norfolk, where there were 500 pairs of sparrowhawks in 1949, by 1965 there was only one pair left.

This collapse in numbers was common with all species until the mid-1960's and the publishing of *Silent Spring*, the now classic book on the environmental impact of agricultural chemicals by Rachel Carson. Many of the more hazardous chemicals were banned and the raptor population started, with some exception, to climb near their post-war numbers.

Some birds of prey are still in decline in the UK. The barn owl population has dropped by 10 percent over the last ten years and continues to fall, probably due to changing farming methods and the introduction of new rat poisons.

WHAT YOU CAN DO

Try and use organic produce: the less pesticide in the system the less danger of another 'Silent Spring'.

USEFUL CONTACTS

The Hawk Trust

The Pesticide Trust

Council for the Protection of Rural England

The Soil Association

Dolphins Threatened by Tuna Fishing

LOCATION

Eastern Tropical Pacific from the Californian coast to Chile, mainly off Central America.

KEY FACTS

Yellowfin Tuna spend most of the time swimming under schools of dolphin, usually Spotted, Spinner and Common. This behaviour is, as yet, unexplained.

In order to catch tuna, fisheries used the dolphin as spotters. When sighting has been confirmed a net is played out around the dolphins and then pulled by cable from underneath, forming a huge purse around the tuna and of course the dolphins.

The Eastern Spinner Dolphin has been so badly decimated that the US now specifically bans shooting nets around them.

The US fishing fleet uses a system called 'backdown', in which the boat reverses and the net sinks low enough to let the dolphins swim out.

Official US figures show that around 99% of the captured dolphins are released but it is estimated that this still leaves around 20,500 dead each year. Injured and dying animals are not included in the death count.

Based on these figures it is estimated that 4 million dolphin are trapped and released each year by the American fleet alone.

WHAT YOU CAN DO

Boycott Tuna products unless they have a recognised 'Dolphin Friendly' label. Ask your supermarket manager to stock only dolphin friendly products

USEFUL CONTACTS

Whale and Dolphin Conservation Society

Greenpeace UK

Earth Island Institute

Environmental Investigation Agency

Wildlife Trade

LOCATION

Worldwide

KEY FACTS

On average, each year the trade ships 4 million birds, 10 million reptile skins, 15 million pelts and 350 million fish. Between 60 and 80% of all live wild animals shipped to markets around the world die during transit.

Of the 300 parrot species, 77 are in danger of extinction and 16 are at risk yet most rare parrots sold are taken from the wild with a survival rate of one in four during transit.

Custom officials in the United States estimated that the illegal trade is worth more than the legal, $300 million as opposed to $250 million.

Each year 200 million Asian bull frogs are killed to supply the western restaurant trade with legs.

Flowers and cacti are also taken from the wild and sold around the world. For example, around one million wild orchids are traded each year.

The illegal trade in animals is worth around $1.5 billion and is a major threat to many endangered animal and plant species.

WHAT YOU CAN DO

This trade only survives because of the demand. Don't buy live animals or their products.

USEFUL CONTACTS

Worldwide Fund for Nature (WWF)

Environmental Investigation Agency

Lynx

Destruction of the African elephant

LOCATION

African sub-continent

KEY FACTS

The African elephant (*Loxodonta africana*) stands up to 4 m high and weighs some 7,500 kg.

In Tanzania numbers have dropped from 100,000 to 29,000 in ten years, mostly due to poaching. In Africa as a whole the population has fallen from 1.3 million to 625,000 over the same period.

In the early 1970's the average weight of a traded ivory tusk was 11 kgs. This had fallen to 9 kgs in 1976 with the trade supplying 812 tonnes or 45,000 elephants. In 1984 the weight had dropped down to around 6 kgs and some 70,000 deaths were needed to meet the same demand since the average age of the elephants was dropping.

In 1989 the price of ivory averaged $200 per kg. It takes 100 elephants to obtain a tonne of ivory.

In 1989 the Convention of International Trade in Endangered Species (CITES) met and agreed to a worldwide ban on the sale of elephant ivory.

WHAT YOU CAN DO

Don't buy any ivory product, many 'antique' pieces are fakes and are made from illegal ivory

USEFUL CONTACTS

World Wide Fund for Nature

Elefriends

The White Elephant Trust

The Environmental Investigation Agency

Care for the Wild

The Hunting of Songbirds

LOCATION

Mediterranean

KEY FACTS

The Royal Society for the Protection of Birds estimate that hundreds of millions of songbirds are being killed annually in the countries bordering the Mediterranean.

Although many are eaten most are illegally killed for sport.

Each year around 250 million birds are killed in Italy, mostly robin, finches, larks, blackbirds and thrushes. The birds are usually netted and trapped.

Around one thousand rare honey buzzards are shot in the Straights of Messina, between, Sicily and mainland Italy, each year during their migration.

In Cyprus alone seven million migrants are caught with lime sticks, small pieces of wood covered with glue.

Article 642 of the Italian Civil Code allows hunters to shoot over any private ground without asking permission this makes enforcement of any protective legislation very difficult.

WHAT YOU CAN DO

The International Council for Bird Protection (ICBP)
is the coordinating body working to stop this
slaughter by fighting for protective legislation in
Europe. They need your help.

USEFUL CONTACTS

ICBP

Royal Society for the Protection of Birds

LIPU UK

Amici de la Terre

The Hunting of Walrus for Ivory

LOCATION

Alaska, North West Siberia and the Aleutian Islands

KEY FACTS

The Pacific walrus population numbers 150,000 to
200,000. Each year the combined Soviet and US
hunts kill 10,000–20,000 animals with around $\frac{1}{3}$ of
the 'kills' lost at sea after being wounded. If the
present rate of hunting continues the entire
population of Alaksan Pacific walrus could be wiped
out by the end of the century.

It has the US law allows aboriginal people of Alaska to
hunt the walrus, only if its done in a 'non-wasteful
way'; but with no quota system. in effect, the law
gives open permission to hunt for ivory.

It has been estimated that fewer than 4% of
walrus killed during the hunting season are taken for
meat with the rest (between 4000–5000) being
hunted only for ivory.

The Pacific walrus is not on the Convention of International Trade in Endangered Species (CITES) endangered list so international trade in the ivory is not illegal.

After each kill the head is removed, usually with a chainsaw, and the rest of the body discarded.

Walrus ivory sells for about $50 per pound with adult tusks weighing 8 to 10 lbs each. Following the loss of the African ivory trade the price of Alaskan ivory rose by 35% in 1989.

WHAT YOU CAN DO

Don't buy any ivory products. With the closing of the African trade walrus ivory is being used in the manufacture of *hankos*, Japanese signature stamps as well as native carving.

USEFUL CONTACTS

Friends of Animals

Earth Island Institute

Enviromental Investigation Agency

The Return of the Antarctic Fur Seal

LOCATION

South Georgia, Antarctica

KEY FACTS

In the late 18th and 19th centuries the Antarctic fur seal was hunted in such numbers that by the beginning of this century there were only a few hundred left.

This tiny population in the early part of the 20th century was rigorously protected by the Falkland Islands Government which allowed the species to reestablish itself on its former sites.

The population on Signy Island, the site of the British Antarctic biological research station, increased from 1 animal in 1948 to 13,350 in 1987.

As the whale population of Antarctica has declined, krill, the small shrimp and principal food of the fur seal, has increased allowing the population to boom.

WHAT YOU CAN DO

The return of the fur seals is an example of what many organisations are working towards. By stopping now we may still be able to pull back many animals and habitats threatened with extinction.

USEFUL CONTACTS

World Wide Fund for Nature (WWF)

Greenpeace International

The Decline in the Northern Isles Seabird Colonies

LOCATION

Shetland and Orkney Islands

KEY FACTS

More than 10% of the UK's Important Bird Areas are in the seabird colonies of the Orkney and Shetland Islands which are recognised throughout the world as a prime breeding areas.

Since 1984 many of the seabird species of the Shetlands, and to a lesser extent the Orkney Islands have suffered a major decline in numbers.

Following detailed studies between 1987 and 1990 it was discovered that many arctic tern chicks were not surviving beyond their first few days due to hunger. At the same time the Shetland sandeel fishery suffered a slump in the catch. Sandeel, which are used in fish meal are the main food source for many of the seabirds, including the arctic tern and puffin.

The sandeel fishery peaked at 52,500 tonnes in 1982 but declined to under 5,000 tonnes in 1988.

In 1989 the Department of Agriculture and Fisheries introduced restrictions on the landing of sandeels, although a connection between the decline of the fishery and bird population has still to be proved. Hopefully it's not too late to save the Northern Isles bird populations.

WHAT YOU CAN DO

Support the work of the campaigning organisations.

USEFUL CONTACTS

Royal Society of the Protection of Birds

The Trade in Rhino Horn

LOCATION

Far East and China

KEY FACTS

Its estimated that there are only 8500 rhino left in Africa and 2005 in India and Java.

In the Far East, where powdered rhino horn is used as a herbal medicine it sells for as much £30,000 per kilo for the Asian and £1,000 for the African horn in the Far East.

The Chinese government has approximately 10 tonnes of rhino horn in stock, representing 3,300 black rhinos.

Although China joined CITES (Convention on International Trade in Endangered Species) in 1981, the World Wide Fund for Nature (WWF) claim that horn is still being smuggled in from Yemen, Hong Kong, Macao and Taiwan.

If this medicinal trade continues, it is estimated that all four species of remaining rhino will be extinct within ten years.

Rhino horn has become so valuable that many collections of antique horn artifacts have been broken up or stolen and sent to the far east.

WHAT YOU CAN DO

Don't buy rhino horn trophies or powdered medicines. In the middle east rhino horn daggers are still for sale.

USEFUL CONTACTS

World Wide Fund for Nature

2 Energy

Global Warming

LOCATION

Worldwide

KEY FACTS

Global warming is caused by the rising level of carbon dioxide and other 'greenhouse' gases which trap heat in the atmosphere. It is almost certain that the build-up of these gases will cause the average world temperatures to raise over the next century.

In a report commissioned by the United Nations in 1990 scientists predicted that if current trends continued, global temperatures would rise between 2 and 5 degrees centigrade by the end of the 21st century.

The main greenhouse gases being emitted today are carbon dioxide, which accounts for 50% of the total, methane, chloroflorocarbons (CFCs), nitrous oxide and ozone.

The most 'efficient' greenhouse gases are the CFCs, which are many thousand times more effective in trapping heat than carbon dioxide. They also damage the ozone layer which protects the planet from ultraviolet rays of the sun.

Some 70% of the world's carbon dioxide emissions comes from the burning of fuels, mostly fossil fuels such as coal, oil or gas.

United Nations scientists estimate that sea levels will rise on average about 60 cm but perhaps by as much as 1 metre by the end of the next century if greenhouse gases continue to be generated at the present rate. This would put at risk the highly populated river basins of the Indian subcontinent, the Nile and many Pacific islands.

WHAT YOU CAN DO

Save energy in the home and workplace – energy saved means less carbon dioxide being produced. Use public transport more. When disposing of a fridge or freezer make sure the CFCs are collected safely. Save energy by recycling paper, glass and aluminium.

USEFUL CONTACTS

Friends of the Earth (International)

Centre for Alternative Technology

Association for the Conservation of Energy

Transport 2000

Energy Efficiency Office

Energy Efficiency

LOCATION

Worldwide

KEY FACTS

Increasing energy efficiency is by far the most cost effective approach to tackling the problem of the rising levels of carbon dioxide (CO_2) and other gases, in the earth's atmosphere, or 'greenhouse effect'. This is because most CO_2 comes from the burning of fossil fuels to produce energy. Through using more efficient appliances, insulating buildings to cut heat loss, and so on, we can reduce energy consumption.

Over the last five years the energy efficiency of the average household appliance has increased by 20 to 30% in the US and 50% in Japan.

As much as 20% of your energy bill can be saved by installing loft insulation. The insulation will usually pay for itself within two or three years.

In Britain, 8% of the electricity produced is used for refrigerators and freezers using £1 billion worth of power. This is the equivalent of two coal burning power stations emitting 15 million tonnes of carbon dioxide per year. By simply producing better insulated refrigerators we can make a dramatic reduction in greenhouse gases.

New legislation in the US outlawing inefficient appliances will save $28 billion by the year 2000 and save building 25 large power stations. If Britain had the same laws 600 megawatts of power could be saved.

WHAT YOU CAN DO

Insulate your home. Use energy saving bulbs and draught proofers. Shop around for energy efficient appliances.

USEFUL CONTACTS

Friends of the Earth

Scottish Campaign to Resist the Atomic Menace (SCRAM)

Energy Efficiency Office

British Coal

Hydro-Electric Power

LOCATION

Worldwide

KEY FACTS

In 1986 hydro-electric power supplied 21% of the world's electricity. North America accounts for around 42%, Europe 36%, Asia 9%, Latin America 8% and Africa 5%.

Hydro-electric dams provide clean, cheap and renewable power. However, unless they are properly managed and sited they can cause huge environmental and social problems.

Between 1973 and 1983 Brazil tripled its hydro-electric capacity with one dam, the Balbina flooding 1554 square kilometres of forest, while the planned Tucurui Dam reservoir will flood another 216,000 hectares.

The Indian government is planning a huge complex comprising 3000 dams. The Namada valley project will force around 1 million people from their homes.

The Ataturk Dam in Turkey, the ninth largest in the world, seriously threatens the viability of hydro-electric schemes downstream in Syria and Iraq. The Iraqis believe that this new dam will further reduce the flow in the Euphrates, forcing the closure of four power plants supplying 40% of the country's power and affecting the irrigation of 1.3 million hectares of farmland and creating further political tension in the Middle East.

WHAT YOU CAN DO

Hydro-electric power is a renewable resource which in some circumstances can provide cheap, plentiful power, but campaigning organisations are fighting the massive, highly costly schemes which have displaced millions of people around the globe and devastate environments.

USEFUL CONTACTS

Friends of the Earth (International)

The International Rivers Network

Scottish Campaign to Resist the Atomic Menace (SCRAM)

Centre for Alternative Technology

Wave Power

LOCATION

Norway, United Kingdom, Denmark

KEY FACTS

Wave power has been used in two prototype generators at Tofteshallen, near Bergen, Norway since 1985 producing energy cheaper than most other forms of generation. In 1988 one of the plants was destroyed by storms.

A 1.5 megawatt station is planned for King Island in the Bass Straights, Tasmania.

Wave power stations are more expensive to build than traditional non-nuclear stations such as coal fired plants, but they are much cheaper to run, as the fuel is free. They should last up to 4 times longer than a nuclear station, that is around 120 years.

Britain's first wave power generating station is on the Hebridean island of Islay.

WHAT YOU CAN DO

Britain has some of the best wave sites in the world yet the wave power programme is chronically under-funded. Write to your government representative urging that resources be put into research.

USEFUL CONTACTS

Friends of the Earth (England, Scotland and Wales)

Greenpeace UK

Centre for Alternative Technology

Scottish Campaign to Resist the Atomic Menace

Energy Reserves

LOCATION

Worldwide

KEY FACTS

At our present rates of consumption we have only 30 years left of proven oil reserves, 40 years of natural gas, and 200 years of coal. These fossil fuels account for 90% of the world's commercial production.

Of the non-renewable resources oil accounts for 32% of annual world energy usage, coal 26% and natural gas for 17%. The rest was made up of nuclear and hydro-electric generation.

The industrialised West burns 70% of the world's non-renewable fossil fuels yet accounts for less than a quarter of the population, while 2.5 billion people, a half of the world's population burn nothing but wood or dung. The United States alone uses a quarter of the world's commercial energy, the Soviet Union around a fifth.

Although more reserves are being discovered they are mostly in remote parts of the globe where extraction is difficult and delivery to markets expensive.

With around 400 million cars now on the planet each one using an average of two gallons per day the demand for fossil fuels is enormous, with the cost being acceleration in global warming and acid rain.

Since the oil price increases of the early 1970s much work has gone into saving fuels. Cars now get 25 miles per gallon more, on average, than they did in 1973 and the total value of energy savings made since then amounts to $250 billion.

WHAT YOU CAN DO

Use the car less and use public transport more. Find out about the energy saving you can make at home. See Energy Efficiency

USEFUL CONTACTS

Friends of the Earth (International)

Energy Efficiency Office

Centre for Alternative Technology

Geothermal Energy

LOCATION

Worldwide

KEY FACTS

Geothermal energy uses the earth's heat as a means of generating power, by pumping cold water down a borehole several kilometres deep and then bringing it back up at boiling point, or simply tapping into a subterranean pocket of steam or boiling water.

Japan has nine geothermal power stations and

due to its seismic activity has the potential to generate up to 30,000 megawatts of power, which could replace 23 nuclear power stations.

The Soviet Union's first geothermal station with an 11 megawatt capacity was built in 1967 in the Far East. They have started a new building programme of another five stations. The total geothermal capacity of the Soviet Union is estimated at 150,000 metawatts.

The first use of geothermal heat in the UK is in the city of Southampton which has a bed of 'hot rocks', 1700 metres below the city.

WHAT YOU CAN DO

Geothermal energy is another renewable energy source which is underfunded. Write to your representative asking that your government make money available.

USEFUL CONTACTS

Friends of the Earth (International)

Greenpeace International

Centre for Alternative Technology

Solar Power

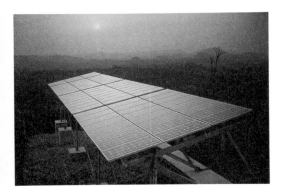

LOCATION

Worldwide

KEY FACTS

Solar power falls into three areas: passive where the heat of the sun is trapped in buildings usually through conservatories or large windows, active where solar heat is used to warm water which is then used to provide heat, and solar cells where the light from the sun is used directly to produce electricity.

The world's largest solar power plant is Solar One, in the Mojave Desert, California. It generates 10 megawatts of electricity using an array of 1800 mirrors. The mirrors reflect the sun's heat into a central boiler whose contents are converted to steam which in turn drives a turbine.

With the efficiency of solar cells increasing and their cost falling many new applications are being found. Cells are now used to power refrigerators and telecommunication sites in many developing countries.

In 1990 the United States Coastguard installed solar cells on 10,500 of its 16,000 navigation beacons making a saving of $2.2 million per year. But very little is being done in the UK.

WHAT YOU CAN DO

Find out whether you can install a passive solar heating system. The Centre for Alternative Technology can supply information.

USEFUL CONTACTS

BP Solar

Friends of the Earth (International)

Greenpeace International

Scottish Campaign to Resist the Atomic Menace (SCRAM)

Centre for Alternative Technology

Tidal Power

LOCATION

United Kingdom

KEY FACTS

There are operating tidal stations in Canada, France, China and the Soviet Union.

The world's first tidal barrage was built across the River Rance, Brittany, France.

Tidal power stations work by using the movement of tidal water as the motive power to drive turbines.

In 1987 it was estimated that tidal power could potentially supply between 15 and 23% of Britain's electricity requirements.

Tidal power is non-polluting, and comparatively cheap. It is estimated that barrages on the Severn and Mersey would create up to 75,000 jobs during the construction phase.

The major disadvantage of tidal barrages is the detrimental effect they would have on the bird life of the river estuaries. In some rivers, like the Severn, 50% of the habitat of wildfowl and waders would be affected.

WHAT YOU CAN DO

Like wave power the development of tidal power has been handicapped by lack of money. Write to your MP asking that further research is carried out.

USEFUL CONTACTS

Royal Society for the Protection of Birds (RSPB)

Centre for Alternative Technology

Friends of the Earth (England)

Friends of the Earth (Scotland)

Greenpeace UK

Wind Power

LOCATION

United States, Denmark, Scotland

KEY FACTS

Wind power now accounts for 1% of the total power requirements of Denmark; the Danish government is aiming for wind turbines to produce 10% of its need by the year 2000.

The largest wind turbine in the world with a 60 foot wingspan, is at Burgar Hill, Orkney. It produces 3 megawatts and supplies 2000 homes.

The biggest group of wind turbines in the world, amounting to 80% of the world total, is at Atamont Pass, California where several thousand machines generate 1500 megawatts of power.

Europe's largest windpark is at Taendpibe, Denmark with 75 machines generating 75 to 200 Kilowatts.

It's estimated that to produce between 10 and 20% of the British power requirements would need 10,000 to 20,000 wind turbines some of which would probably be sited offshore.

WHAT YOU CAN DO

Urge your electricity generating company to invest in more wind turbines.

USEFUL CONTACTS

Friends of the Earth (International)

Greenpeace International

Centre for Alternative Technology

Scottish Campaign to Resist the Atomic Menace (SCRAM)

3 Consumerism

Alar

LOCATION

United Kingdom and United States

KEY FACTS

Alar is a pesticide containing daminozide, a plant growth regulator which encourages growth in apple trees, reddens the apples and makes the fruit easier to pick. It's also used on grapes.

It's estimated that Alar was used on 5% of the US apple crop and 7% of the British crop.

Toxicity studies in the US in the early 1980s showed that a byproduct of daminozide, unsymmetrical dimethyl hydrazine (or UDMH) could, in some circumstances, cause tumours in mice. Residues of UDMH were also found in apple products such as apple juice and apple sauce and because Alar was used on the developing buds, it entered the fruits and couldn't be washed or peeled off.

In January 1989 pressure groups in the US estimated that as children under the age of six are likely to eat more fruit and vegetables than the rest of the population, they may develop between 5500 and 6000 more cancers due to pesticide residues, and that the UDMH in Alar is likely to be responsible for around 1100 of these.

As a result of these findings Alar was banned in the US in February 1989, following a ban in New Zealand.

Although this evidence appeared in the US, in May 1989 the Advisory Committee on Pesticides for the British Ministry of Agriculture said that Alar did not pose a health risk to consumers.

Following further research by the manufacturers, Uniroyal announced in October 1989 that they would halt sales worldwide as the product could no longer provide 'clean data'.

WHAT YOU CAN DO

The Alar controversy highlights the problems with pesticides – try and buy organically produced foods.

CAMPAIGNING ORGANISATIONS

The Pesticide Trust

Parents for Safe Food

The Soil Association

Aluminium Waste Recycling

LOCATION

Worldwide

KEY FACTS

In the US 40% of all aluminium cans are made from recycled materials. In Sweden the figure is 90%, but in the UK only 8%.

In 1988, 5.6 billion cans were used and disposed of in the UK – enough to reach the moon and back!

When aluminium cans are recycled the energy saved can be as high as 95% with a 95% cut in air pollution.

At 1990 prices scrap aluminium was worth around 50 pence or US$1 per kilo.

A 50% recycling rate of all aluminium cans would reduce annual bauxite consumption by 232,000 tonnes.

WHAT YOU CAN DO

Collect and deliver all your used aluminium cans to a central depository. Or start one yourself at school or in your workplace.

USEFUL CONTACTS

Friends of the Earth (England and Wales, Scotland)

Aluminium Can Recycling Association

Can Makers Information Service

Dioxins

LOCATION

Worldwide

KEY FACTS

Dioxins, some of the most toxic chemicals known, are produced as a byproduct of various chemical reactions, such as the bleaching of paper pulps in paper manufacture, the production of herbicides and insecticides and during plastic and pharmaceutical manufacture. Almost all forms of combustion, from fossil-fuelled power stations and car engines to domestic fires, produce dioxins.

Some dioxins are so toxic that many believe that it is impossible to establish a level of exposure that could be regarded as safe.

Tests have shown that dioxins are the most carinogenic of all toxins, producing a whole range of cancers and increasing the carcinogenic qualities of other chemicals.

Dioxins are not biodegradable, and continue to be a threat to the environment for many years. They have been found 20 years after they were first sprayed as a herbicide.

During the Vietnam War a defoliant called Agent Orange was used to clear the jungle routes of the North Vietnamese Army. This herbicide was contaminated by dioxins and went on to produce birth defects and poisoning in the sprayed areas.

WHAT YOU CAN DO

Use paper products that have not been chlorine bleached. Try to eat organic produce.

USEFUL CONTACTS

Women's Environmental Network

Greenpeace International

Friends of the Earth (International)

Disposable Nappies

LOCATION

Western Europe and North America

KEY FACTS

During the first two and a half years of a baby's life its nappy will be changed an average of 5475 times. As 1000 nappies can be produced from a pine tree, each baby will need five and a half trees which take on average 40 years to grow!

Disposable nappies are not biodegradable. The outer and inner linings are made from polyethylene and polypropylene.

A random survey taken by the Nappy Advisory Service showed that 63% of local authorities had problems caused by disposable nappies being flushed down the lavatory.

Dyna-rod, the drainage specialists, estimate that 7% of its calls to private homes involved nappy blockages, while in the United States it is estimated that they cause 95% of sewerage blockages.

WHAT YOU CAN DO

Use the traditional British terry napkin or a combination of both. When using disposables, dispose of them carefully, with solid rubbish in your dustbin, not flushed down the toilet.

USEFUL CONTACT

Women's Environmental Network

Nitrate Contamination of Water Supplies

LOCATION

Southern England

KEY FACTS

In the UK the use of nitrogen fertilizer has risen from 60,000 tonnes in 1938 to 1.5 million tonnes in 1985.

When too much nitrogen is used the excess is washed off the fields by rain, contaminating the water table and ultimately drinking water.

In areas of heavy nitrogen use, more than 150 kg of nitrogen per hectare can be leached into the water table. Nitrates have been linked to stomach cancer and other illness.

As well as being a threat to public health, they cause river weeds to grow excessively and may be causing algal blooms around the coasts.

Over 1 million people in England regularly drink water which exceeds the EC limit for nitrates.

The British government has introduced a pilot monitoring scheme in ten areas of the UK. Where nitrogen levels are close to or above the EC limits, farms in the chosen areas will be offered advice on how to reduce the levels of leaching. In order to keep levels low in some cases, they may also be offered financial help towards changing their type of operation.

WHAT YOU CAN DO

Lobby your national representative. Demand uncontaminated drinking water.

USEFUL CONTACT

Friends of the Earth (England and Wales)

Nuclear Power

LOCATION

Worldwide

KEY FACTS

Around the world there are now 426 nuclear power stations in 27 countries accounting for 17% of the world's electricity or 309,564 megawatts.

In France 75% of power comes from nuclear stations, in Belgium 61%, South Korea, Sweden and Hungary about 50% while in the US and the UK it is around 20%.

Since 1957 there have been 10 major accidents at nuclear plants ranging from a reactor fire at Windscale, in Britain, a near meltdown of the core at Three Mile Island, US and the explosion at Chernobyl, in the Soviet Union.

The nuclear industry produces three types of waste: low, intermediate and high level. Britain produces around 25,000 cubic metres of low-level waste per year mostly in the form of contaminated protective clothing and laboratory equipment. Intermediate waste accounts for 1000 cubic metres annually, and high-level waste 100 cubic metres.

Since the banning of sea dumping in 1983 all low and intermediate-level wastes have been building up at land sites awaiting an agreed safe disposal system, while the high level wastes are stored in cooled tanks at Sellafield, where they will be held for 50 years then encased in glass and stored underground.

WHAT YOU CAN DO

Join the campaign against nuclear power.

USEFUL CONTACTS

British Nuclear Fuels Ltd (BNFL)

Friends of the Earth (England and Wales)

Campaign for Nuclear Disarmament (CND)

Greenpeace UK

Scottish Campaign to Resist the Atomic Menace

(SCRAM)

Sanitary Protection Products

LOCATION

United Kingdom

KEY FACTS

Sales of sanitary protection products were £126 million in 1986 in the UK, jumping from £80 million in 1980, with products ranging from sanitary towels and tampons to incontinence pads.

These products are mainly made of wood pulp, which is some cases has been bleached with chlorine during manufacture, producing dioxin. They may also have been treated with absorbency agents and wet strength agents such as polysorbate and urea formaldehyde. Traces of the chemicals used can remain in the product which unless it is designated as a maternity pad or hospital dressing is not sterilised.

Since 1989 the Women's Environmental Network (WEN) has been campaigning successfully for the reduction in chlorine in the manufacture of sanitary towels and highlighting the environmental consequences of their manufacture and disposal.

The sheer number of sanitary towels being disposed of through the sewage system causes problems as does the non-degradable plastic strips and polythene liners they contain. WEN estimates that 75% of all blockages in public places are caused by the disposal of sanitary towels.

WHAT YOU CAN DO

Use products that have not been bleached. Support the work of the Women's Environmental Network. They can give full details of alternatives.

USEFUL CONTACT

Women's Environmental Network

Air Pollution

LOCATION

Cities worldwide

KEY FACTS

Air pollution levels, from vehicles and industries in many of the world's cities is so bad that it affects health, buildings and water supplies.

In Upper Silesia, Poland, 1000 metric tonnes of dust falls on every square kilometre, with the residents of Katowice province suffering from a 15% higher rate of circulatory illnesses, a 47% higher rate of respiratory ailments and 30% more cancer, than the rest of Poland.

It is estimated that air pollution in Hungary, where 30–40% of the population live in areas of severe air pollution, will cost the country $374 million in illness and premature deaths.

The factories in the Chinese province of Benxi produce 213,000 tonnes of smoke and dust, and 87 million cubic metres of gas each year. The Chinese urban population is four times more likely to contract lung cancer than its rural equivalent.

Although California has some of the world's

strictest emission laws, in 1988 the air quality in the southern part of the state, including Los Angeles, fell below the US health standards on 232 days and was so bad on 75 days that people with heart conditions, respiratory illness and school children were advised to stay indoors.

In an effort to cut down vehicle emissions many cities are now restricting the movement of cars. Florence, Rome, Budapest and Athens have all introduced systems banning cars from the city centres at some time of the day.

WHAT YOU CAN DO

Use public transport, walk or cycle. Fit a catalytic converter to your car and use lead free petrol. Use the car less.

USEFUL CONTACTS

Friends of the Earth (International)

World Health Organisation

Healthy Cities

Polski Klub Ecologiczney

Campaign for Lead-free Air (Clear)

Transport 2000

Acidification

LOCATION

Europe, eastern United States and Canada

KEY FACTS

Each year 100 million tonnes of sulphur, in the form of sulphur dioxide, are released into the atmosphere. It is further oxydised in rain and absorbed by rain droplets to fall as sulphuric acid. Another contributor to acidification is nitrogen oxide produced from the exhaust emissions of cars.

Two-thirds of the UK's annual 3.8 million tonnes of sulphur dioxide emissions are produced by coal-fired power stations.

In Germany acid rain has damaged 55% of all trees, with some of the southern German states losing 90% of silver birch trees.

Acid rain damage to Cologne Cathedral is now costing £1.5 million per year.

Due to prevailing winds three-quarters of the sulphuric acid falling in Norway and Finland was produced in Britain.

In Sweden, 18,000 lakes have been completely acidified; 30 species of lichen and 12 mosses have declined or disappeared along with the disappearance of fish.

In part of Pennsylvania acid rain is 1000 times more common than pure water.

In 1990, members of the EC agreed to cut sulphur dioxide levels gradually over the next 20 years but there is still a long way to go.

WHAT YOU CAN DO

Try and use less electricity. Be more energy efficient. Cut down on the use of your car.

USEFUL CONTACTS

Friends of the Earth (International)

Greenpece International

Transport 2000

Asbestos

LOCATION

Worldwide

KEY FACTS

Asbestos is commonly found in older public buildings and factories where until recently it was widely used as an insulator, strengthener and as fireproof roofing material.

Made up of minute mineral fibres, it can be fatal or cause chronic illness if inhaled.

Of the three most common types of asbestos,

blue, brown or white, blue and brown have been banned. White is still used but its packaging must contain a health warning.

Asbestos causes three main illnesses, lung cancer, asbestosis or severe scarring of the lungs and mesotheliomia, a rare chest cancer, all of which can take a long time to develop, up to 40 years in some cases.

In 1985 it was estimated that 80% of the buildings owned by the metropolitan authorities had asbestos somewhere in their fabric.

WHAT YOU CAN DO

Asbestos sheeting and lagging are still common in older buildings so seek advice from your local authority before moving or cutting.

CAMPAIGNING ORGANISATION

Society for the Prevention of Asbestosis and Industrial Diseases

Car Pollution

LOCATION

Worldwide

KEY FACTS

Cars produce a number of emissions which are damaging both to health and to the environment as a whole. These include carbon monoxide, hydrocarbons, nitrogen oxides and ozone.

Motor transport produces 85% of the UK's total carbon monoxide pollution, 28% of hydrocarbons, 45% of its nitrogen oxides and 15% of carbon dioxide.

A three-way catalytic converter fitted on a car turns carbon monoxide to carbon dioxide, hydrocarbons become carbon dioxide and water, while the nitrogen oxides become nitrogen. It works by passing the harmful gases over a honeycomb coated with a very thin layer of precious metal which triggers a chemical reaction.

In 1989 2.7 million new cars were sold in the UK, and by the year 2025 it is estimated by the government that there will be $2\frac{1}{2}$ times more traffic on British roads.

The American taxpayer subsidises motoring by $27 billion each year, while in Sweden it is estimated that cars cost the country around 11 billion kroner annually.

Traffic planners in Los Angeles estimate that if they double deckered their whole freeway system of 4000 kilometres it would be congested within 15 years.

Cars produce up to 5 tonnes of carbon dioxide, use up to 2000 litres of oil and need around 1.2 tonnes of steel in their manufacture.

They kill, or injure around 40,000 people each year in the UK.

WHAT YOU CAN DO

Use the car less, share journeys, convert to lead free petrol. If you buy a new car make sure a catalytic converter is fitted.

USEFUL CONTACTS

Healthy Cities

Transport 2000

Friends of the Earth (England and Wales; Scotland)

Food additives

LOCATION

Worldwide

KEY FACTS

75 % of the food sold in the UK and the US contains some sort of additive with each person in the UK now eating three ounces of additives per week.

Food additives have been used from the earliest times- the Romans coloured their bread white; the Egyptians and the Aztec's of Central America both used cochineal in foods.

Additives are used in many ways in the food industry, from preserving meats to colouring peas.

Not all additives are added to processed foods. In order to produce deep golden eggs yolks, battery hen feed includes a colouring agent which can dye the yolk any colour the consumer wants. The producer can offer a range from pale yellow to the golden, free range yellow.

Farmed trout and salmon are fed the colouring agent cantaxanthin to produce pink fleshed fish. This colouring in the wild would be supplied from their various food sources.

Studies in the US have shown that by reducing food additives and by eating less processed foods behavioural problems in prisoners were reduced, and school children's academic performance increased dramatically.

WHAT YOU CAN DO

Check the labels on processed foods. Do you know
what the E numbers are? Eat more organically
produced foods.

USEFUL CONTACTS

Parents for Safe Food

The Vegan Society

The Vegetarian Society

Glass Recycling

LOCATION

Worldwide

KEY FACTS

Glass containers form about 10% of household
rubbish: 6000 million glass containers are used in
Britain each year but with only 16% recycled. In the
Netherlands the figure is 60% while in Switzerland
it is 50% and France 25%.

Producing new glass from glass cullet or old,
saves around 25% of fuel and it can be done many
times without loss of quality.

In Britain there is, on average, one bottle bank
for every 16,000 people while in the Netherlands it is
one for every 2,000.

WHAT YOU CAN DO

Save all bottles and jars. Return all deposit paid
bottles. Find out where your nearest bottle bank is.
Remove all tops and caps from bottles before putting
them in a bank. Separate coloured bottles and jars
and make sure they go in the appropriate hole in the
bottle bank. If there is no bottle bank near you
contact your local authority.

USEFUL CONTACTS

Friends of the Earth (England and Wales; Scotland)

British Glass Manufactures Association

United Glass

Green Tourism

LOCATION

Worldwide

KEY FACTS

Green tourism or ecotourism is one of the growth sectors of the travel business with the figures increasing dramatically each year.

Fewer than 10,000 people visited Nepal in 1965 but by 1987 the figure had risen to 240,000, mostly to go trekking in the Himalayas. Although tourists have greatly increased Nepal's foreign exchange revenue, they have caused erosion on mountain paths and the increased need for fuelwood has added to the general deforestation.

Tourists visiting Rowanda's mountain gorillas in the Parc des Volcan now account for one-third of the country's foreign exchange and have financed the further protection of the gorillas.

In a survey conducted by the World Wide Fund for Nature it found that more than half of the tourists polled in Latin America had visited at least one ecological site or national park.

In 1989 2500 tourists visited Antarctica but proposals are being made in Australia to build a centre in the Vestfold Hills near the Davis station that would accommodate 16,000 visitors per year complete with a 2800-metre runway capable of taking a jumbo jet!

WHAT YOU CAN DO

As you can see not all 'green tourism' is good. Plan your holiday carefully: you may be destroying the very thing you came to see. Friends of the Earth (Cyprus) are researching new ways of managing green tourism in their island.

USEFUL CONTACTS

World Wide Fund for Nature (WWF)

Royal Society for the Protection of Birds (RSPB)

Friends of the Earth (Cyprus)

Landfill Waste Disposal Sites

LOCATION

Western Europe and the United States

KEY FACTS

The biggest rubbish dump in the world is the New York, Fresh Fields landfill site which accepts waste 24 hours per day, every day of the year. It covers 3000 acres with 26,000 tonnes added daily. When the site is full in ten year's time it will be the highest point of land between Maine and Florida.

Once household waste is dumped, the rotting process produces gases. Typically, one tonne of waste

produces 400 cubic meters of gas, 60% highly
explosive methane and 40% carbon dioxide. Both
methan and carbon dioxide contribute to the
greenhouse effect

It is estimated that in the UK there are 500 waste
tips where methane gas leakage could cause a threat
to public health and the cost of making them safe
would be £250,000.

Methane from disposal sites can be collected and
used as an energy source. This was first exploited at
Palos Verdes, California in 1975 and in Britain 30
sites are now being tapped.

WHAT YOU CAN DO

Produce less rubbish, recycle as much as possible.
Buy less packaged goods.

USEFUL CONTACTS

Friends of the Earth (International)

Lead in Drinking Water

LOCATION

United Kingdom

KEY FACTS

Over 8 million homes in the United Kingdom have
lead-contaminated domestic water supplies. This
represents about 45 of all households in the country
although it is in the areas of soft water that lead pipes
corrode and contaminate the supply.

Scotland, with its soft water, has the largest
proportion of the population living in old housing
stock and affected by lead in drinking water.

Children are most at risk from lead poisoning.

Effects include low birth weight, lack of concentration and learning difficulties.

Lead piping and storage tanks are usually only found in houses built before 1964 although many houses built after this date had copper pipes joined with lead solder. The use of lead solder is now being phased out.

WHAT YOU CAN DO

If you live in an old property, replace your lead tank, a grant is available. Use bottled water or water from a non-lead supply to make up baby feeds. Ask your local authority to test your supply.

USEFUL CONTACTS

Friends of the Earth (Scotland)

Glasgow For People

Lothian and Edinburgh Environmental Partnership

Organic Farming

LOCATION

Europe, United States

KEY FACTS

Over 20,000 farmers in the United States already use organic methods.

Organic farming helps control soil erosion, improves the tilth of the soil and reduces the chances of pesticide and nitrogen residues entering the food chain.

Research in the US shows that water erosion removed 32.4 tonnes of soil per hectare on a 'conventional' farm while on an organic farm it was reduced to 8.3 tonnes.

Erosion is one of the greatest threats to American farming: in 1982 the US Department of Agriculture produced figures showing that 44% of arable land was at risk from erosion. In 1986 the Soil Survey of England and Wales also showed 44% of arable land at risk.

According to the journal New Scientist, if erosion continues at present rates, topsoil will eventually become so thin that fertilizers will fail to increase yields and then they will begin to decline

Organic farms use 40% less fossil fuels than conventional farms to produce crops of the same value.

WHAT YOU CAN DO

Buy organic produce not only will you be consuming less chemicals but you will be helping to keep the earth's soil in good heart.

USEFUL CONTACTS

Friends of the Earth (International)

Henry Doubleday Research Association

The Soil Association

The Vegetarian Society

Bio-dynamic Agricultural Association

Pesticides

LOCATION

Worldwide

KEY FACTS

A pesticide is a material used in the control or elimination of plants or animals.

Around 800 compounds are used as pesticide, ranging from simple organic materials such as plant extracts to synthetic inorganic compounds.

Its estimated that in one year, 1986, over a billion gallons of pesticide spray was used in Britain and in 1987 26.5 kilogramme of active ingredients, or nearly a quarter of a pound per head of population, worth over 409 million in sales.

In 1983, approximately 26 million acres of land were treated with pesticides with many crops receiving multiple doses.

It's estimated that the poisoning of bees by pesticides costs around US$150 million in lost honey production and crop pollination, while the losses from the poisoning of domestic animals and the contamination of meat and milk cost around US$15 million per year.

In the United States there are some 45,000 pesticide poisonings annually resulting in 50 fatalities, and that 20,000 people each year are victims of pesticide induced cancers.

Everyone is exposed to some degree to pesticides either directly or indirectly through residues in food and water. Many of the pesticides banned or severely restricted in their country of origin, usually in the West, are frequently available in the Third World.

WHAT YOU CAN DO

Try to use organically grown foods. Wash all fruit and vegetable thoroughly.

USEFUL CONTACTS

Friends of the Earth (England and Wales)

The Pesticides Trust

Green Alliance

Plastic Recycling

LOCATION

Worldwide

KEY FACTS

The UK produces around 1.3 million tonnes of
plastic packaging each year yet salvages only a few
hundred tonnes. Plastic packaging accounts for
around 7% by weight or 20% by volume of
household waste.

Although the E C produces around 10% of the
world's total plastic production of 100 million
tonnes, it has no integrated recycling scheme. A
recent scheme in Coburg, Germany had to be
abandoned because not enough plastic, 5 tonnes per
day, could be found to keep it going economically.

In Britain there are 60 firms who specialise in recycling plastic producing 50,000 tonnes of black polyethylene film and 25,000 tonne polypropylene (used in the manufacture of plastics pipes etc.)

Recycling of plastics is difficult because so many different types are used and no efficient method of sorting has yet been developed. In Sheffield, where a demonstration project is underway as part of Recycling City, the plastics are being sorted by hand. So far the quickest machine to do the job sorts three containers per minute.

WHAT YOU CAN DO

Try to use less plastics. Use a shopping bag. Buy soft drinks in glass or aluminium containers. Many supermarkets will now take back used plastic bags. Ask your local manager to introduce a scheme.

USEFUL CONTACTS

Friends of the Earth (England and Wales; Scotland)

British Plastics Federation

Lothian and Edinburgh Environmental Partnership

(LEEP)

Wastewatch

Paper Waste Recycling

LOCATION

Worldwide

KEY FACTS

Pulping waste paper to make recycled paper gives an energy savings of up to 50%.

Recycling paper reduces the need for plantation forestry which can have many damaging environmental effects. Each year we each use the equivalent of two trees worth of paper.

Around 90 million trees are cut down annually to meet the paper and board requirements of the U K, with 2.2 tonnes of wood required to produce 1 tonne of paper.

The average British household throws away around 3 kg of paper each week.

Since the mid-1950's all glovebox interiors of Mercedes-Benz cars have been made from recycled paper!

WHAT YOU CAN DO

Use recycled paper products, encourage your family and employers to do the same. Collect your household paper and return it to a central collection point for recycling. If there isn't a paper bank near you ask your local authority to provide one.

USEFUL CONTACTS

Friends of the Earth (England and Wales; Scotland)

Institute of Waste Management

Wastewatch

Earth Island Institute

Lothiand and Edinburgh Environmental Partnership (LEEP)

The Safe Disposal of Engine Sump Oil

LOCATION

Worldwide

KEY FACTS

Used car engine oil collects lead and other poisonous petrol additives, such as phosphorus, magnesium and zinc which are released into the atmosphere when the oil is burned.

Each year approximately 1.25 million tonnes of waste oil enters the world's oceans.

Around 830,00 tonnes of lubricating oil are used in the UK each year with between 50,000 and 100,000 tonnes unaccounted for.

Most spent oil is used in garage space heaters. In the UK this accounts for 40,000 tonnes per year which is burned without any restriction. It should only be burnt in special equipment designed to restrict pollution.

WHAT YOU CAN DO

Never pour used oil down a drain or onto the ground. Collect the oil and deliver it to the local authority amenity site. Encourage your authority to provide this service.

USEFUL CONTACTS

Friends of the Earth (England and Wales)

Smoking

LOCATION

Worldwide

KEY FACTS

According to the World Health Organisation (WHO), smoking now kills around one million people each year and causes chronic illness to millions more. In Britain diseases related to tobacco kill around 100,000 people per year.

Living or working beside a heavy smoker can increase a non-smokers chance of developing lung cancer by as much as 30% according to the UK's Independent Scientific Committee on Smoking and Health.

A cigarette smoker has up to a three times greater chance of having a heart attack than a non-smoker, and men under the age of 45 who smoke have up to a 15 times greater chance of having a heart attack than non-smokers.

Women who smoke during pregnancy tend to have babies around 200 grams lighter than non-smokers and the risk of stillbirth or death during the first week increases in relation to the numbers of cigarettes smoked.

In most developed countries, more teenage girls than boys are starting to smoke resulting in increasing lung cancer deaths in women. In Scotland, for example, it is now the leading cause of deaths in women.

Although tobacco use is falling in the West, it is still rising in the third world by around 3% per year.

The Chinese government estimate that if the present trends in smoking there continue, by the year 2020 lung cancer will kill one million a year. In 1989 the Chinese smoked their way through a third of the worlds cigarettes, with consumption rising from 500 billion to 1600 billion in ten years. On present smoking patterns about 50 million of those now aged under 20 will die from smoking related illnesses.

WHAT YOU CAN DO

Try to stop smoking. Ask your employer to ban smoking from the workplace.

CAMPAIGNING ORGANISATIONS

Action on Smoking and Health (ASH)

National Society for Clean Air

The Reclamation of Used Batteries

LOCATION

Worldwide

KEY FACTS

Most batteries contain metals such as lead, cadmium and mercury. As the casing corrodes these toxic metals are released into the environment.

In an effort to reduce these metals levels the EC has ruled that the level of mercury in batteries should be reduced to 0.025% by weight by 1992.

Due to the many types of battery available it may be some time before satisfactory recycling schemes can be introduced.

In draft proposals the EC has favoured a deposit scheme on the sale of all new batteries, the money being returned when exchanged for the spent batteries.

Car batteries can be recycled and some garages or scrap dealers will take them.

WHAT YOU CAN DO

Encourage your local authority to set up battery collection schemes.

USEFUL CONTACTS

Friends of the Earth (England and Wales)

Use of Detergents and Washing Powders

LOCATION

Worldwide

KEY FACTS

Modern washing powders and detergents contain a wide variety of ingredients which can be harmful to the environment, such as phosphates, bleaches, optical whiteners and enzymes.

Phosphates act as a fertilizer when they eventually find their way from the kitchen to the sea via the sewage systems. Many rivers suffer from annual algal blooms caused by too much phosphate in the water. Although there are several other sources of phosphates, for example human sewage and agricultural run-off, detergents contribute up to 30% of the total.

Optical brighteners are added to washing powders solely to give an illusion of whiteness. Laboratory tests have shown that they restrict growth and cause mutations in microorganisms.

Enzymes have been known to be an irritant to the skin and cause asthmatic reactions.

During the breakdown of chlorine bleach, which is mostly found in dishwasher powders and toilet cleaners (and are not normally an ingredient of washing powders), different kinds of organo-chlorine substances are produced some of which are known to be highly toxic.

WHAT YOU CAN DO

There are alternative detergents available such as Ecover or Ark – try them.

USEFUL CONTACTS

The Ark Trust

Ecover

Pollution from Aircraft and Rockets

LOCATION

Worldwide

KEY FACTS

New research has shown that the nitrogen oxide exhaust emitted by supersonic aircraft, or high-speed civil transport (HSCT), could seriously damage the ozone layer.

It has been estimated that a fleet of 500 supersonic aircraft could deplete the ozone layer by as much as 20% and even with more efficient engine systems they would still have a major effect.

NASA spent $25 million dollars in 1990 investigating ways to overcome the environmental problems caused by super sonic transport including ozone destruction and noise levels.

New interest has been shown both in Japan and Europe in developing a new generation of faster, larger and cheaper types of supersonic passenger aircraft capable of making the journey from New York to Tokyo in six hours. These technological 'advances' would cause large ammounts of pollution

Each of the Space Shuttle's boosters releases about 75 tons of hydrogen chloride into the upper atmosphere eventually destroying ozone molecules.

Soviet scientists estimated that a single shuttle flight can destroy up to 10 million pounds of ozone and that 300 shuttle flights over a five year period could destroy the ozone layer.

WHAT YOU CAN DO

Find out more information from the campaigning organisations

USEFUL CONTACTS

Friends of the Earth / Les Amis de la Terre (Canada)

Friends of the Earth (United States)

4 Animal Welfare

Animal Experimentation

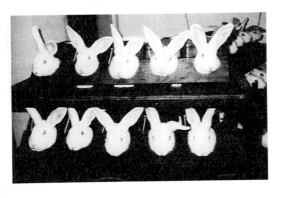

LOCATION

United Kingdom

KEY FACTS

In 1988, 3.5 million animals ranging from monkeys to mice, died as a result of laboratory experiments. Approximately 13,000 dogs, mostly beagles are used in British laboratories each year.

In Britain in 1987, 111,313 animals were used in LD50 tests. These tests involve calculating the dose-level which will kill half the animals in a test group by giving progressively greater dose levels.

Even 'cruelty free' products are likely to have

been tested on animals at some time. Many manufacturers are now using the results of earlier animal experiments, in order that no further animal testing need be done.

Drugs such as Thalidomide and Eraldin were passed as safe for human use after extensive animal testing.

WHAT YOU CAN DO

Use only 'cruelty free' products. Make a point of asking for them in your local shops

USEFUL CONTACTS

Royal Society for the Prevention of Cruelty to

Animals

The Society for the Prevention of Vivisection

Animal Aid

Animal Liberation Front

FRAME

British Union for the Abolition of Vivisection

Battery Hens

LOCATION

United Kingdom

KEY FACTS

There are 38 million egg-laying chickens in Britain and 96% of them are kept in cages. The government recommends 450 square centimetres as the minimum living space for a each bird. This is less than a sheet of A4 paper. With cages measuring 18 × 20 inches it means four or more birds to a cage.

Conditions are so cramped that the birds are unable to stretch their wings.

Egg-laying birds are not only crowded but have their beaks cut to stop them injuring their neighbours. They live for around 18 months and produce 200 eggs per year.

In Britain there are 400 million broilers at any one time, kept in sheds holding 20,000 birds. A broiler goes from hatching to slaughtering seven weeks never once leaving the shed. Their weight goes from a few ounces to $4\frac{1}{2}$ pounds in 50 days. As the weight increase's, living space becomes progressively more cramped.

WHAT YOU CAN DO

Only buy free range eggs and chicken. Ask your supermarket manager to stock them.

USEFUL CONTACTS

Chicken's Lib

Parents for Safe Food

Royal Society for the Prevention of Cruelty to

Animals

The Vegetarian Society

Compassion in World Farming

Pig Production

LOCATION

United Kingdom

KEY FACTS

Pregnant sows are confined in steel pens for the whole of their $3\frac{1}{2}$ month pregnancy. The pigs cannot turn, have difficulty lying down and have no physical contact with other pigs.

Once she has given birth a sow is placed in a steel farrowing crate to prevent her from crushing the young pigs and so cutting their profit margins. In the wild, a pig would build a 'nest' for her new piglets.

After seven days she is again mated and the cycle continues. In her life time she will produce on average 10 litters until she is 'spent' and at the age of five goes for slaughter.

The piglets are reared for 14 weeks until they reach 100 lbs and are slaughtered for pork or bacon.

WHAT YOU CAN DO

Don't eat pork or bacon unless you know it comes from a free range, organic source. Ask your butcher to get free range carcasses.

USEFUL CONTACTS

Parents for Safe Food

Royal Society for the Prevention of Cruelty to

Animals

The Vegetarian Society

Compassion in World Farming

Animal Aid

Salmon Farming

LOCATION

Norway, Scotland

KEY FACTS

Production of Atlantic salmon in Scottish fish farms has gone from 1000 tonnes to an estimated 54,000 tonnes in 1991. It is worth more to the Scottish economy than beef and sheep production combined.

In order to control the salmon louse, fish growers use the agent Nuvan which was developed as a pesticide for use in the control of insects. Nuvan is known to be very poisonous to other marine invertebrates. Tests have shown that molluscs die within 24 hours after doses of only 1 part per million.

Salmon farms attract a wide range of predators, including seal, otter, mink, heron, cormorant and shag. Their control by netting and shooting has caused concern.

It is estimated that for every 100 tonnes of food used, one tonne of solid waste sinks to the seabed, contaminating the surrounding environment.

Unlike wild salmon, the flesh of the farmed variety is grey and is made pink by adding a synthetic dye to the foodstuff twelve weeks before marketing.

WHAT YOU CAN DO

Remember that farmed salmon contains additives its not as 'pure and natural' as you think.

USEFUL CONTACTS

Scottish Wildlife and Countryside Link

(A group of twelve leading Scottish environmental bodies)

Scottish Salmon Board

The Atlantic Salmon Trust

Turkey meat production

LOCATION

Western Europe and United States

KEY FACTS

The production of turkey meat is one of the food industry's growth areas – in 1988 33.5 million were slaughtered commercially.

Male turkeys are bred to be so heavy and 'meaty' that they can no longer mate naturally. Artificial insemination is commonly practised throughout the industry. Once their fertility drops the parent birds are slaughted and processed into turkey meat products.

Rearing turkeys intensively can induce severe strains in the flocks: they peck at each other's toes, feathers and eyes and will resort to cannilbalism which is a major problem in the industry. ،

Debeaking or beak trimming is used to discourage aggressive behaviour in the turkey rearing sheds, some of which may hold up to 15,000 birds. Debeaking is done with a red-hot blade when the chicks are a few days old.

Due to selective breeding many of the male birds, which weigh up to 60 lbs, can develop diseases of the hipjoints and legs other diseases which affect the birds include Blepharo-conjunctivitis which attacks the eyes, and colisepticaemia which damages the liver necessitating the widespread use of drugs.

WHAT YOU CAN DO

Boycott all forms of turkey meat. Write to your national representatives to tell them of your concern.

CAMPAIGNING ORGANISATIONS

Chicken's Lib

Compassion in World Farming

The Vegetarian Society

Vegetarianism

LOCATION

Worldwide

KEY FACTS

Vegetable food production uses land more
efficiently. An area the size of 5 soccer fields would
give enough maize to feed 10 people, wheat for 24
people, soya beans for 61 people and meat for only 2
people.

An average Briton eats 8 cows, 36 pigs, 36 sheep
and 750 poultry in a lifetime. Over half of the meat
comes from animals which have been fed growth
promoting hormones and most poultry and pork is
produced intensively on 'factory farms'.

Meat eaters have 30% more heart disease, five
times greater likelihood of missing work or being
hospitalised, and higher blood pressure.

Of the world's 40 poorest countries, 36 export
food to the US most of which goes on cattle feed
During the Ethiopian famine, Britain imported
grain from Ethiopia to feed cattle. We are starving
other countries so that we can have a meat diet.

WHAT YOU CAN DO

Reduce your intake of meat products. If you eat meat, only buy free range products. Eat more fish and other proteins such as beans and pulses.

USEFUL CONTACTS

The Vegetarian Society

Parents for Safe Food

The Vegan Society

5 World Resources

Driftnet Fishing

LOCATION

The Pacific Ocean, from the coast of Alaska to east of New Zealand.

KEY FACTS

Each night in the Pacific fishing fleets shoot 30,000–40,000 miles of drift net, with each boat setting between 9 and 30 miles of net. The intended catch is mainly squid, and some salmon and trout.

The nets are so big they catch everything in their path, including, whales, seals , seabirds and porpoises. It is estimated that these nets cause the deaths of up to 100,000 marine animals and 1 million seabirds annually.

Drift nets are banned by many nations of the Pacific basin in the territorial areas but are still used by hundreds of boats in unregulated international waters.

Lost nets, called 'ghosts', continue to fish for years catching anything that they come in contact with and only sinking when the weight of entangled creatures becomes too great.

In the South Pacific the nets used to capture the albacore, a type of tuna, are 15 meters deep and 56 kilometres long. 45.000 tons of albacore can be taken in one season.

WHAT YOU CAN DO

Support the work of the agencies fighting for a ban on this type of fishing.

USEFUL CONTACTS

Sea Shepherd

Greenpeace International

Earth Island Institute

Environmental Investigation Agency

Whale and Dolphin Conservation Society

Logging of Virgin American Forests

LOCATION

Pacific Northwest-USA and Canada

KEY FACTS

On the North American continent 95 % of the virgin forest has been destroyed with nine-tenths of the total cut on the Pacific Northwest coast.

These temperate rain forests contain some of the largest trees in the world; the sequoia grows up to 274 feet tall and to a diameter of 25 feet. Although the rain forest of the tropics contains a greater variety of species the average plot on the Pacific Northwest has twice as much plant material.

The coastal redwoods, threatened by continued logging grow only in an area limited by the reach of the ocean mists.

In Canada less than one-twentieth of the ancient forest is protected; logging now takes place in the provincial park on Vancouver Island where only one-quarter of the virgin forest survives.

Japan is the biggest single customer with most of the wood going for ply or pulp products.

WHAT YOU CAN DO

Ask your timber supplier to use only material from managed plantations, not from the wild.

USEFUL CONTACTS

The Sierra Club

The Audubon Society

IWW-Earth First!

Antarctica

LOCATION

The whole of the Southern Ice Cap.

KEY FACTS

Antarctica covers one-tenth of the world's surface and harbours a unique wildlife population. On average Antarctica's ice sheet is 1,600 metres thick, extending up to 4,000 metres; it covers 98 of the continents surface and extends over $5\frac{1}{2}$ million square miles. It is one of the last unspoilt places left on the planet.

In 1989, at the meeting of the Antarctica Treaty in Paris, Australia and France, with the support of Italy proposed that there should be a complete ban on mining and mineral extraction on the continent of Antarctica. They were opposed by the UK; Germany, the US and Japan who all wanted to allow oil prospecting.

Antarctica is the habitat of 50% of the earth's seals and the breeding ground for 100 million birds.

The ecosystems of Antarctica are so delicate that even a footprint left in the moss that grows in the short summers would take 14 years to disappear.

WHAT YOU CAN DO

Ask your national representative to support the Antarctica World Park movement

USEFUL CONTACTS

Greenpeace International

Friends of the Earth (International)

World Wide Fund for Nature (WWF)

The Antarctica Project

British Antarctic Survey

Desertification

LOCATION

The desert zones of the world

KEY FACTS

Desertification is caused by a number of factors but they commonly fall into the areas of overgrazing, deforestation and overcultivation usually as the result of abandoning traditional farming techniques.

About 3,500 million hectares of land worldwide are affected by desertification . Each year 6 million hectares are lost with another 21 million hectares lost from economic crop production.

Those African nations most effected by the encroachment of the desert have the highest percentages of malnourished children. These are Burkina Faso, Ethiopia, Chad, Mali, Angola, Mauritania, Somalia and Niger. In Burkina Faso 40% of the children are underweight.

Between 1958 and 1975 the edge of the Sahara, in Sudan, has moved 100 km south.

WHAT YOU CAN DO

Support the organisations trying to halt the expansion of the deserts.

USEFUL CONTACTS

Green Deserts

Oxfam

Friends of the Earth (International)

War on Want

Intermediate Technology

Wetlands Destruction

LOCATION

Worldwide

KEY FACTS

The world's wetlands, swamps, bogs, tidal estuaries etc., provide a habitat for thousands of plants and animals, and are among the most productive ecosystems on earth, covering around 6% of the land surface.

As well as providing a spawning ground for two-thirds of the world's fish catch, these wetlands have the capacity to filter out many types of pollutants by acting as a gigantic sieve.

Vienna, Calcutta and part of the southern US use marshlands as a means of purifying their water or treating sewage-many see this as a an economic method for giving many Third World nations cheap clean water.

Around the globe it's estimated that between one-half and one-quarter of marshlands and swamps have been destroyed. Between 1950 and 1970 the US lost 185,000 hectares of wetland annually and the state of Iowa lost 99% of its marshes mainly to agriculture. Yet wet lands can produce up to eight times as much plant material as wheat field.

In many developing countries many of the most productive wetlands are now under threat from hydroelectric schemes and cattle ranching.

In response to these types of threats a conference was convened at Ramson, in Iran which set out to protect the wetlands; it called upon its signatories to conserve and promote the sound utilisation of its wetlands.

WHAT YOU CAN DO

Press your local and national representatives to add more sites to the Ramson registration list.

USEFUL CONTACTS

Royal Society for the Protection of Birds (RSPB)

Worldwide Fund for Nature (WWF)

Destruction of the Tropical Rainforests

LOCATION

The Tropical Rainforests cover 9 million square miles or 7% of the Earth's surface. They are located in the monsoon areas between the Tropics of Cancer and Capricorn.

KEY FACTS

These forests are being destroyed at a rate of 2% per year – an area the size of England and Wales. At the present rate they will be totally destroyed by the year 2025 except for remnants in Zaire and Amazonia.

The timber trade accounts for around 25% of the destruction, yet it only sells, on average 2–3% of the timber cut.

The expansion of cattle ranching, the major cause of forest destruction, in Latin America, means the loss of 2.5 million hectares of forest a year, mainly to supply the fast food industries of western Europe, North America and Japan with cheap beef.

The forests contain half of all the known species of the world's animals and insects. Only 1% of rainforest plants have been investigated for their economic potential.

The forests already provide us with bananas, rubber, sugar, pineapple and many other fruits. The drug curare, used in cardiac surgery, and in the treatment of multiple sclerosis and Parkinson's disease is derived from a South American rainforest plant. The United States National Cancer Institute has identified more than 2000 tropical rainforest plants with the potential to fight cancer.

Although the soil of the forest supports the largest variety of life on the planet, it is usually of very poor quality. Its fertility comes from the action of microorganisms and insects which quickly reduce fallen leaves and the droppings of animals into a rich compost but this fertility cannot survive in the absence of the forest.

In South America, the opening of service roads into the forests, has been followed by an influx of landless peasants. Although their crops tend to do very well in the first few seasons the quality of the soil drops quickly unless increasing amounts of fertilizers are used.

In 1950 there were 40 million square kilometres of untouched forest areas in the world; this declined to 26 million square kilometres by 1978. It is projected that this figure will fall to 22 million by the year 2000, if the present destruction rate is continued.

Japan, the worlds biggest market for tropical hardwood, has increased its demand twenty-fold between 1950 and 1974. The United States, the second largest buyer, imports around $1 billion worth a year, while western Europe accounts for 40% of the world trade.

The destruction of these great forests would mean losing up to half of the Earth's lifeforms. Potentially there exists many valuable crops and medicines. The rainforests act like vast lungs converting carbon dioxide into oxygen. Treeroots bind the thin soils stopping erosion and flooding, while the canopy reflects heat from the surface of the globe. Lose the rainforests and we may lose the planet.

WHAT YOU CAN DO

Boycott tropical timber. Ask for temperate substitutes. Write to you local and national representatives asking them to support the campaign. Infortrmation on alternatives is available from Friends of the Earth.

USEFUL CONTACTS

Friends of the Earth (International)

Survival International

Green Deserts

Loss of Genetic Plant Material

LOCATION

Worldwide

KEY FACTS

Many ancient varieties of crop plants are being lost as more and more marginal land is being cleared and farmed. These plants contain the genetic potential to breed new disease-and pest-resistant crops.

One quarter of the world's plants are in danger of becoming extinct within the next 25 years. Over the last 40 years at least 95 % of all the ancient wheats of Greece have disappeared.

One small colony of wild rice in central India provided the only known gene resistance to a stunting virus. That resistance was subsequently bred into the most commonly grown rice variety.

Modern farming techniques, the widespread use of herbicides and the reliance on two or three varieties of 'supercrop' have all contributed to the decline of wild stock.

It's proposed that an international 'seed bank' be set up in a disused mineshaft in Spitzbergen, inside the Arctic Circle.

WHAT YOU CAN DO

Encourage your local fruit and vegetable supplier to stock a wider range of local foods such as apples, pears and potatoes. There are hundreds of varieties of English apple yet we only buy about three.

USEFUL CONTACTS

International Board for Plant Genetic Resources

Parents for Safe Food

Destruction of Mangrove Forests

LOCATION

Tropical coastlines

KEY FACTS

Mangrove forests provide breeding grounds for fish, stabilise shorelines and are a unique habitat for many plants and animals.

Two-thirds of the world's fish are hatched in mangrove and tidal areas which around the world cover an estimated 240,000 square kilometres. Almost 80% of the fish taken from the Ganges and the Brahamaputra rivers come from the forests.

Mangrove forests are being destroyed by the timber industry and fish farming; they are being poisoned by agricultural pesticide run-off. The most serious destruction is taking place in Asia – the Philippines forest has been reduced from 146,000 hectares in 1980 to 38,000 hectares mostly destroyed for the woodchip industry. In Australia, US and Caribbean, mangroves are being lost to tourism.

WHAT YOU CAN DO

Although the destruction of mangrove forests seems a remote problem they are as valuable as rainforests. Support the campaigning organisations trying to preserve them.

USEFUL CONTACTS

Earth Island Institute

Friends of the Earth (Australia)

WALHI-Indonesian

Sahabat Alam Malaysia

National Parks

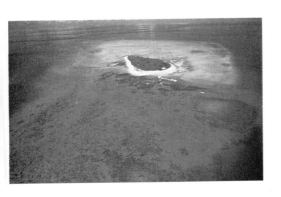

LOCATION

Worldwide

KEY FACTS

Since the world's first nation park was set up at Yellowstone, in the United States in 1872 the idea has spread around the globe. Today 3% of the earth's land surface now covers a reserved area of some kind. The World National Park Congress would like to see this area raised to 10%.

The protected areas are varied, consisting of 25% tundra, 19% tropical dry forests, 15% semi deserts, 12% tropical rain forests and 29% other types of ecosystems.

Throughout the world there are 90 World Heritage Sites which are designated and protected by their contracting states as sites that have important natural or cultural significance for the whole world. These range from Mont St Michel in France to the Ngorongoro Crater in Tanzania.

Although some of the most famous sites such as the Great Barrier Reef and Mount Everest are protected, more areas are needed.

WHAT YOU CAN DO

Visit your national parks and persuade your national representative to protect more land. Support the protection of land for nature conservation. National parks are not the only way of doing this but they do have a part to play.

USEFUL CONTACTS

World Wide Fund for Nature

The Countryside Commission

Over exploitation of world fish stocks

LOCATION

Worldwide

KEY FACTS

Of the 22,000 species of fish found in the oceans and seas of the world only 22 are caught in amounts exceeding one million tonnes.

Since 1950 fishing catches have quadrupled, rising from 20 million tonnes to 92 million tonnes. Over 33% of the total world catch is converted to animal feed or oils. In 1980 nine nations accounted for 58% of the world's total catch.

The United Nations Food and Agriculture Organisation has stated that if the annual world catches exceed 100 million tonnes, the seas could be reaching their maximum sustainable catch.

Of the 280 world fisheries listed by the United Nations, only 25 are classified as under or moderately exploited; the rest are reaching their maximum level of exploitation.

One of the most dramatic examples of overfishing was the Peruvian anchovy catch which fell from 12 million tonnes in 1974 to 100,000 tonnes in 1983.

The consequence of this uncontrolled pillaging of the seas has been the rapid decline of existing stocks with some species nearing extinction resulting in the severe disruption of local economies.

WHAT YOU CAN DO

Try to eat only locally caught fresh fish. Exotic species, ie non local, are now being imported to Europe and the US in larger quantities.

USEFUL CONTACTS

World Wide Fund for Nature (WWF)

Greenpeace International

Ozone Layer Destruction

LOCATION

Worldwide

KEY FACTS

Although at ground level ozone is a pollutant, in the stratosphere, at 12 kilometres and more above the earth's surface, where it is as rare as 10 parts per million, it filters out much of the sun's harmful ultra violet radiation.

When an ozone (O_3) molecule in the stratosphere is hit by ultra violet radiation, it is split into O_2, an oxygen molecule and a free oxygen atom O. It is this split which converts the radiation into heat, stopping it reaching the earth's surface. The O and O_3 recombine to form ozone and the cycle continues.

The ultra violet ozone cycle is being destroyed by CFCs or chlorofluorocarbons and other chemical in the upper atmosphere.

Cloroflorocarbons are used as propellants in aerosol cans, coolants in refrigerators and air conditioning units, solvents used for cleaning electrical circuit boards and making plastic foam containers used in the fast food industry.

Although CFCs are being banned around the world as aerosols propellants, million of tons are still being produced, and further millions are still in use in older refrigerators and air conditioners.

Exposure to excess ultra-violet causes cataracts, skin cancers and damage to the skins immune system.

The US Environmental Protection Agency predicts that for every 1 percent of drop in global ozone, the levels of skin cancer would increase by 1 to 3 % They estimate that over the last ten years destruction of the ozone layer caused an extra 4 million skin cancer cases worldwide.

WHAT YOU CAN DO

Don't use any product containing CFC's or other
ozone damaging chemicals Ask your local authority
to safely reclaim the coolants from used refrigerators
and air conditioners.

USEFUL CONTACTS

Friends of the Earth (International)

Greenpeace International

Loss of Coral Reefs

LOCATION

Tropical seas

KEY FACTS

Coral reefs are one of the most densely populated of all the ecosystems and probably the oldest. Most are between 5,000 and 10,000 years old and are built on a much older and thicker core probably millions of years old.

Major damage is being done to coral reefs around the world – from tin mining and fish farming in Thailand and Malaysia, to boat damage in the Caribbean.

In the Phillipines, 44,000 square kilometres of coral reef, supporting one-tenth of the country's fish catch is under threat from the degradation of habitat caused by fertilizer run-off.

The Pennekau reef, at Key Largo Florida has 3 million visitors each year around half of whom dive on the reef, over 4000 per day. The reef is seriously polluted by oil from boat engines, litter and discarded fishing lines.

Of the 109 countries with significant reefs 93 are damaged.

The Australian government estimate that the Great Barrier Reef earns $90 million per year while in the Bahamas coastal tourism accounts for one half of the GNP.

WHAT YOU CAN DO

Don't buy coral products, or if visiting a reef don't remove pieces as mementos.

USEFUL CONTACTS

The Sierra Club

Friends of the Earth (US)

Earth Island Institute

Greenpeace International

Preservation of Peatlands

LOCATION

United Kingdom

KEY FACTS

Scotland has some of the most important peat bogs in the world, accounting for almost two thirds of the British total and one tenth of the world's.

Peat bogs are a unique habitat and are host to a range of specially adapted birds, plants and insects. Dunlins, golden plovers and greenshanks, bog rosemary and bog myrtle, and several types of moths and butterflies are among the species threatened by the destruction of the bogs.

The 'flow country' or blanket bogs of Caithness and Sutherland are very rare in world terms and have been recognised in the World Conservation Strategy of 1980 as a priority area for protection.

By 1987 about 70,000 hectares or one-sixth of the total area of peatland in Caithness and Sutherland had been overplanted with forestry. Another 100,000 hectares may be afforested in the future.

Britain imports about 50% of its peat with around 80% of that coming from Ireland. Britain also imports from the Soviet Union where 200 million tonnes are extracted each year.

WHAT YOU CAN DO

Don't buy any peat based product, a list of alternatives is available from Friends of the Earth (Scotland). Ask your garden centre or garden shop to stock alternatives.

USEFUL CONTACTS

Friends of the Earth (Scotland)

World Wide Fund for Nature (WWF)

Royal Society for Nature Conservation

Henry Doubleday Research Association

Arms Spending

LOCATION

Worldwide

KEY FACTS

Arms spending now stands at $2.7 billion per day with the Soviet Union, the US and their allies accounting for 73% of the total.

Up to 1983 the Soviet Union, China, Saudi Arabia and Israel spent more on the military than they did on education or health.

During the same period Canada and Sweden spent the equivalent of under $500 per person on arms while Saudi Arabia spent $2686.

Ethiopia spends around 10% of its gross national product on defence and 1.5% on health care, while the Swedes spend 2% on defence and 15% on health and education. On average each nation spends 6% of its gross national product on defence.

Worldwide, there is more money now spent on defence per year than the total income of the poor, $2.5 billion dollars per day.

In the US 70% of all public funds spent on research and development are on military projects, in the Soviet Union the figure is 60% while in the UK it accounts for 50%.

WHAT YOU CAN DO

Ask your national representatives to support cuts in arms spending.

USEFUL CONTACTS

Oxfam

Campaign for Nuclear Disarmament (CND)

The relocation of the Hupla

LOCATION

West Papua, Indonesia

KEY FACTS

Following an earthquake in 1989, which killed 100 people, the Hupla tribal people of the Woso valley, West Papua were moved by the Indonesian government to a lowland site.

The Hupla, who were not all consulted on the move, were told that they wouldn't receive relief aid unless they left their ancestral homeland.

The resettlement area is already owned by another tribe and is infected by tropical diseases to which the Hupla have no resistance. Already many people have died from malaria and malnutrition.

Although many Hupla want to return, the Indonesian government has continued to offer inducements of consumer goods and food to remain.

It's thought that the traditional Hupla lands are rich in mineral resources.

WHAT YOU CAN DO

Support the campaigning organisations by writing to the President of Indonesia complaining about the treatment of the Hupla.

USEFUL CONTACTS

International Work Group for Indigenous Affairs

(IWGIA)

Survival International

The Destruction of the Yanomani Indians

LOCATION

North West Brazil

KEY FACTS

Out of a total population of 9,000, 15% of the Yanomani Indians have died since 1987. At this rate, the entire population will be wiped by the end of the century.

During the early 1970's, the first roads were pushed into Yanomani lands in the remote northwestern corner of Brazil. Although the road was not completed it brought in settlers who introduced new illnesses such as influenza, measles and venereal disease which decimated the population of villages on the route with 90% mortality in some places.

The discovery of tin and gold mines on the Indian lands brought in a flood of 'garimpeiros' or independent gold prospectors. With 45,000 mines supported by 120 illegal airstrips supplying the new 'industry'.

The Indians are not only dying from diseases. Mercury, from the mine workings has polluted rivers, killing fish and wildlife, the basis of Indian food. In one region 90% of the indian population suffers from malaria.

WHAT YOU CAN DO

Support the work of Survival International. Write to the President of Brazil and the Governor of Roraima expressing your concern over the fate of the Yanomani. Full address in listing.

USEFUL CONTACTS

International Work Group for Indigenous Affairs

(IWGIA)

Survival International

Fuelwood Crisis

LOCATION

Developing countries - worldwide

KEY FACTS

Wood as a domestic fuel is used by two billion people around the globe, 70% of whom don't have secure supplies.

Half of all the wood cut throughout the world is used for fuel, and the average daily use is about 3 kilos per person. Trees are now being destroyed faster than they can regrow causing massive deforestation in the areas where they are most needed.

Due to the shortage, traditional alternative sources are being used in many countries; animal dung, for example is burned, which then leads to a fertilizer shortage. As one tonne of animal manure can produce 50 kilos of grain the effect of removing this source of fertilizer can be dramatic. In Nepal the use of dung as a fuel has cut local grain yields by as much as 15%.

It is estimated that to meet the demand for fuelwood 2.7 million hectares of trees have to be planted per year as opposed to the 555,000 hectares planted at the moment.

Not all fuelwood is used by rural populations; much is converted into charcoal and sold in cities. The World Bank estimates that by the year 2000 up to three quarters of all West African fuelwood will be used in cities.

WHAT YOU CAN DO

Support the campaigning organisations. Many are trying to introduce renewable fuel sources and more efficient simple stoves.

USEFUL CONTACTS

Green Deserts

Intermediate Technology

Oxfam

Baltic Sea Pollution

POLLUTION TO BE HALTED?

KEY FACTS

Research by the Swedish Environmental Protection Agency, has shown that 100,000 square kilometres or one-third of the Baltic seabed is lifeless. It is thought this destruction is caused by massive influx of nitrogen and phosphorus from the surrounding coastlines causing algal blooms and oxygen loss.

This high level of nitrogen causes eutrophication (growth due to excess nutrients) and is the greatest threat to the Baltic. One of the major sources of nutrient pollution is from the River Vistula in

Poland which discharges the same amount of nitrogen as the combined run-off from the whole of Sweden.

Two of the Baltic's most important cod spawning grounds, the Gdansk and Gotland Deeps are suffering from severe oxygen depletion, which reduces the hatching rate and subsequent fish numbers.

The International Stockholm Environmental Institute has estimated that there are around 200 'hot spots' around the Baltic where the nutrient levels should be reduced by between 65 and 90%.

In 1980 a bloom of toxic algae 10 meters deep and 10 kilometres wide developed in the Kattegat and Skagerrak areas at the mouth of the Baltic. Over 200 kilometres of coastline were affected causing massive fish deaths and beach closures.

WHAT YOU CAN DO

Support the campaigning organisations trying to get the Baltic cleaned up.

USEFUL CONTACTS

Coalition Clean Baltic (CCB)

Estonian Green Movement

Swedish Environmental Protection Agency

Swedish Society for Nature Conservation

Polski Klub Ecologiczney (Poland)

Damming of the River Danube

LOCATION

Austria, Hungary and Czechoslovakia

KEY FACTS

Following massive public opposition the Hungarian government cancelled the Nagymaros Dam scheme on the River Danube. The scheme, part of a joint project between Austria, Czechoslovakia and Hungary, would have been the largest water diversion ever conducted in Europe, rerouting 30 kilometres of the Danube, and providing a three-dam electricity generating system.

Under threat were 30,000 hectares of unique habitat in the Sziegetkoz region of Hungary, and the Csallokoz region of Czechoslovakia, which is home to many rare birds, animals and fish.

Following the cancellation of the Hungarian component of the scheme the Czech government has threatened to build their own second dam which would have the effect of completely stopping the Danube from entering Hungary.

The original scheme was financed by Austria who negotiated an agreement which gave them up to 70% of the scheme generating capacity.

Hungary now is expected to pay in excess of $200 million in compensation to both the Austrian and Czechoslovakian governments. Many environmental organisations are now lobbying the World Bank to offset the cost to Hungary.

WHAT YOU CAN DO

Ask your national representative to get your government to help offset the Hungarian costs. Ask the World Bank to help.

CAMPAIGNING ORGANISATIONS

Foundation to Protect the Hungarian Environment

International Rivers Network

SZOPK

Freunde der Erde (Austria)

World Wide Fund for Nature (Austria)

Mediterranean and Adriatic Sea Pollution

KEY FACTS

Half of the 100 million people who live on the Mediterranean coast live in towns or cities causing heavy coastal pollution with two-thirds of the sewage pumped into the Sea left untreated.

Criss-crossed by busy sea lanes, with tankers carrying 400 million tonnes of oil per year, many areas of the Mediterranean, especially around North Africa are heavy polluted by oil.

It is estimated that 450 million tonnes of waste are dumped annually in both the Mediterranean and the Adriatic with around 1 million tonnes of oil spilled. Other pollutants dumped around the Mediterranean include, 1400 tonnes of lead, 950 tonnes of chromium and 5000 tonnes of zinc.

In the northern Adriatic, at the mouth of the River Po, phosphate levels are ten times higher than in Mediterranean areas. These concentrated nutrients are thought to cause algal blooms, such as the massive outbreak of 1989, which covered beaches along both the Italian and Yugoslavian coasts cutting the tourist trade by one-third.

The coastal areas of the Mediterranean are the most popular tourist areas in the world with Spain alone hosting 55 million visitors per year.

WHAT YOU CAN DO

Think twice about holidays in the Mediterranean. What damage would you be causing?

USEFUL CONTACTS

Greenpeace International

Amici de la terra (Friends of the Earth, Italy)

Friends of the Earth (Cyprus)

The Narmada River Project

LOCATION

Central India

KEY FACTS

The Indian government, with the help of the World Bank, are building what is probably the largest water project in history: 30 major dams, 135 medium dams and 3000 smaller dams on the 800-mile Narmada River and its 41 tributaries in the states of Gujarat, Madhya Pradesh and Maharashtra. The project is intended to provide drinking and irrigation water to drought-prone central and western India.

It is estimated that this project will flood over 400,000 hectares of land and displace one million people including 50,000 tribal people. One dam alone, the Indra Sagar will flood an estimated 90,000 hectares while another, the Sardar Sarovar, will displace 70,000 people.

After sustained protest both in Japan and India, where hundreds of thousands of people have taken to the streets, the Japanese government withdrew its financial support for the Sardar Sarovar project from the World Bank, amounting to $20 million.

The Narmada scheme has been heavily criticised around the world for its poor planning and appraisal of its environmental and social impact. It has been called 'India's greatest planned environmental disaster'.

WHAT YOU CAN DO

Write to the World Bank Executive Director asking him to stop funding the project. Address in the organisational listings.

USEFUL CONTACTS

International Rivers Network

Friends of the Earth (International)

Asia-Pacific People's Environment Network

(APPEN)

North Sea Pollution

KEY FACTS

Although the North Sea has one of the most productive environments in the world, it is heavily polluted.

In 1984 a report produced for the first Conference on the Protection of the North Sea, found that more than 70 million tonnes of sewage sludge, harbour drainings and industrial waste found their way into the the the sea each year. In addition, 1.5 million tonnes of nitrates and 100,000 tonnes of phosphates were washed in annually.

Ten tonnes of mercury, 12 tonnes of cadmium, 1250 tonnes of lead and 200 tonnes of copper are dumped in the North Sea each year.

Britain is now the only country bordering the North Sea still dumping sewerage sludge.

In 1987 a second North Sea Conference resulted in agreements to cut the dangerous inputs into rivers by 50%, to phase out completely incineration at sea by 1994 and to end the dumping of toxic waste by 1989.

WHAT YOU CAN DO

Support your national pressure group. Ask your representatives to support the cleaning up of the North Sea.

USEFUL CONTACTS

Bund (Germany)

Friends of the Earth (England and Wales; Scotland)

Greenpeace International

Vereniging Milieudefensie (Netherlands)

Werkgroep Nordzee Foundation (Netherlands)

Pollution of the River Rhine

LOCATION

Central Western Europe

KEY FACTS

The Rhine, which rises in the Alps, picks up effluent from factories in Switzerland, Liechtenstein, Austria, France, Germany and the Netherlands. Each year the Rhine dumps 10 million cubic metres of silt in the port of Rotterdam. This silt, which is removed by the Dutch authorities is so contaminated that it cannot be deposited at sea but is stored at a special site. This silt contains over 50,000 artificial chemical compounds.

In 1986 at Schweizerhall, near Basle a fire broke out in a warehouse containing 1000 tonnes of chemical products. The water used to extinguish the fire washed between 10 and 30 tonnes of the chemicals into the Rhine causing massive fish loss and threatening all life in the river.

In 1990 a new computer-controlled monitoring system was introduced by the Dutch national water authority, which checks the water quality at twelve stations.

WHAT YOU CAN DO

The Rhine is one of the major rivers flowing into the North Sea one of the most polluted seas in the world. Support the campaigning organisations trying to do something about it.

USEFUL CONTACTS

BUND (Germany)

Vereniging Milieudefensie (Netherlands)

Greenpeace International

The Tehri Dam Project

LOCATION

Uttar Pradesh, India

KEY FACTS

The Tehri Dam when completed will be the single largest dam in Asia, holding back around 3.5 cubic kilometres of water and flooding the Bhagirathi valley for 45 kilometres and another tributary, the Bhillunguna, for 35 kilometres.

The dam, which is estimated to cost $2 billion will flood the town of Tehri as well as another 72 villages, displacing more than 80,000 people and flood 270,000 hectares of the most fertile land in the region.

Many seismologists believe that there is a serious risk of large earthquakes in the valley within the lifetime of the dam and that there is a real danger of the dam being destroyed and inundating the towns down river.

WHAT YOU CAN DO

Support the campaigning organisations by writing letters of protest to the Indian minister of state for the Environment. Address in the organisational listings.

USEFUL CONTACTS

International Rivers Network

Friends of the Earth (International)

Asia-Pacific People's Environment Network (APPEN)

Water Pollution in Eastern Europe

LOCATION

Poland, Hungary, Germany, Czechoslovakia and
the Soviet Union

KEY FACTS

In Hungary, 3000 towns and villages with 800,000
people have no potable water. The permitted levels
of organic matter are three times greater than
allowed in the West.

In Czechoslovakia, 70% of the rivers are heavily
polluted and 28% contain no live fish. Diseases such
as typhus, cholera and dysentery break out regularly.

In Poland, the Vistula River contains 5000 tons
of phosphorus, 90,000 tons of nitrogen, 150 tons of
oil and 3 tons of phenol.

In the Soviet Union the construction of the
Leningrad Barrier an 18-mile long dyke intended to
protect the city from flooding has led to the
degradation of the Neva River and Lake Ladoja.

WHAT YOU CAN DO

Support the campaigning organisations. Ask your
national representative to support environmental
aid.

CAMPAIGNING ORGANISATIONS

BUND (Germany)

DELTA (Soviet Union)

Estonian Green Movement (Soviet Union)

Polski Club Ekologiczny (Poland)

VAK

SZOPK

Water Shortages

LOCATION

Worldwide

KEY FACTS

The demand for water has increased at least four times since the turn of the century and it is estimated that within fifteen years demand will exceed supply in many areas of the world.

The World Watch Institute predicts that there will be major shortages by the year 2000. Since 1980 more than thirty countries have been involved in international disputes over water supplies.

In China, 50 cities face acute shortages with the water table of the North China Plain dropping between one and two metres per year.

Israel, Jordan and the West Bank are expected to be using all renewable sources by 1995.

Serious water shortages now affect some areas in the Unites States. For example, the Ogalalla Aquifer which is the underground source for an area stretching from Dakota to Texas, is seriously depleted. It is thought the levels have dropped by 70% due to the demands made by irrigation schemes and beef ranching.

Since 1941, Los Angeles has been taking 15% of its water from Mono Lake near the Yosemite National Park causing the level to drop by forty feet.

The dropping of water levels on the Aral Sea, Soviet Union has caused serious water shortages 120 miles away.

WHAT YOU CAN DO

Water is a precious resource; use less of it.

USEFUL CONTACTS

Oxfam

War on Want

Green Desserts

Friends of the Earth (International)

International Rivers Network

Clean Drinking Water

LOCATION

Developing countries – Worldwide

KEY FACTS

Around half the population of the developing world do not have access to clean, safe, drinking water. Contaminated water kills 25 million people each year, three-fifths of them young children.

Billharzia affects 200 million people, 500 million have trachoma and 4.6 million children die from diarrhoea, all caused by using dirty water.

Clean water would eliminate half of the world's diarrhoea cases and most of the cholera. Hand washing after defecation reduces outbreaks of diarrhoea by 40% but where clean water is scarce, this is rarely carried out.

In developing countries water consumption is between 350 and 100 litres per day, but where water is scarce this drops to as low as 2 litres.

In India, water-related illnesses account for a loss of 73 million work days per year at a cost of $1 billion in lost production and medical expenses.

Until 1983, a United Nations clean drinking water programme brought clean supplies to 345 million people around the world. Due to lack of funding the rate of installation has dropped.

WHAT YOU CAN DO

What you can do Write to your government representatives asking them to support the United Nations programme.

USEFUL CONTACTS

Oxfam

World Health Organisation

Intermediate Technology

Green Deserts

7 Disasters

Bhopal Disaster

LOCATION

Madhya Pradesh State, India

KEY FACTS

Following the leak of methyl isocyanate, at the Union Carbide plant on the evening of 2nd December 1984, 2,500 people were killed and 250,000 were left disabled.

By 1987, 526,000 citizens of the city had lodged compensation claims against Union Carbide.

Homicide charges were filed in November 1987 against former Union Carbide chairman Warren Anderson and other company officials.

In early 1989 the company agreed with the Indian government to pay compensation worth $470 million as long as all criminal charges were dropped. In 1988 the net profits of Union Carbide were $720 million.

Following a change in government the deal collapsed as the then Prime Minister V. P. Sigh felt that this figure under-compensatated the victims and did not hit the company hard enough.

WHAT YOU CAN DO

Like the disasters at Chernobyll and Three Mile Island, the Bhopal tragedy could have been averted. Although we can do very little now except support the victims through the campaigning organisations, it should serve as a warning for the future.

USEFUL CONTACTS

Sahabat Alam Malaysia (Friends of the Earth,

Malaysia)

Bhopal Victims Support Committee

Chernobyl

LOCATION

Kiev, Ukraine, Soviet Union

KEY FACTS

In the explosion at the Chernobyl nuclear power station in 1986, 4% of the radioactive material in the reactor was released into the atmosphere.

Following the initial explosion in the reactor a radioactive, plume was released It blew northwest, passing over Byelorussia, Latvia and Lithuania and then on to Poland and Scandinavia.

Following a change in the wind direction the plume left a trail 2000 kilometres from the source and was detected in 20 other countries. The radioactive cloud reached the southeast coast of Britain on 2 May, with the highest doses received in Cumbria, Shetland, Wales, Northern Ireland and south west Scotland.

Thirty-five people were killed during and after the explosion trying to contain the radioactivity and fires.

A 30 kilometre exclusion zone has been established around the power station with 135,000 residents evacuated in an area of 10,000 square kilometres around the plant-60,00 people were moved within 24 hours of the accident. All top soil to a depth of one metre and all trees for two kilometres around the site have been removed.

A year after the accident, the Soviet authorities revealed that 500,000 people in Byelorussia, to the north of Chernobyl, had been contaminated along with a fifth of the republic's agricultural land.

The accident has cost the Soviet Union in excess of £5000 million with £500 million paid in individual compensation.

WHAT YOU CAN DO

Don't let it happen again. Join the campaign to stop nuclear power.

USEFUL CONTACTS

Scottish Campaign to Resist the Atomic Menace (SCRAM)

Campaign for Nuclear Disarmament (CND)

Friends of the Earth (International)

British Nuclear Fuels Ltd (BNFL)

The Destruction of the Aral Sea

LOCATION

Soviet Central Asia

KEY FACTS

Between 1973 and 1989 the Aral Sea dropped from the fourth to the sixth largest lake in the world with a loss of water equal to 112 times that of Lake Erie.

The Aral Sea fishery once supported 60,000 jobs, but the fish stocks are now so depleted that the Soviet government now brings frozen fish from Murmansk, 1700 miles away to keep the industry going.

The draining of the sea was caused by the construction of the Kara Kun irrigation canal, which at 850 miles long is the longest of its kind in the world. It was built to water the vast Soviet cotton industry. The two rivers which drain into the Aral, the Syr and the Amu, the largest in the Central Asia, have been diverted to feed the canal and are now virtually empty of water at their outlet with the sea.

Since the mid-1960's the Aral has lost 40% of its surface area or nearly 28,000 square kilometres.

During the peak of production, one town on the banks of the Aral produced 3% of the Soviet Unions entire annual fish catch. Now all of the 24 native fish species are extinct.

WHAT YOU CAN DO

The Aral Sea and its surrounding environment probably cannot be returned to its original state but it serves as a warning of the type of major environmental catastrophe that can happen when longterm environmental are not considered deeply enough.

USEFUL CONTACTS

International Rivers Network

Exxon Valdez

LOCATION

Bligh Reef, Prince William Sound, Alaska, USA

KEY FACTS

On 24 March 1989, the oil supertanker Exxon Valdez leaked 232,000 barrels of crude when it hit a submerged reef, the biggest incident of this kind in US history.

The two year old tanker was en-route to Long Beach California after picking up 1.2 million barrels from the Alaska pipeline.

Exxon, the tanker owners, took ten hours before starting work on the spillage, by which time high winds and choppy seas had turned the oil into a tar like emulsion – 75% oil and 25% water – which made it extremely difficult to treat with dispersants.

As the oil spread throughout the Sound, it devastated habitats and killed many marine animals and seabirds, including the sea otter.

The total body count, up to July 1989 was 84 bald eagles, 844 sea otters and 26,000 seabirds. Seals and sealions were not included as they usually sink without trace.

WHAT YOU CAN DO

Like the other environmental disaster this could have been avoided support the organisations trying to make sure it doesn't happen again.

USEFUL CONTACTS

Friends of the Earth (US)

Friends of the Earth / Les Ami(e)s de la Terre (Canada)

Greenpeace International

The Sierra Club

Earth Island Institute

Three Mile Island

LOCATION

Middletown, Pennsylvania, US

KEY FACTS

At 4 a.m. on the morning of 28 March 1979 feedwater pumps failed in the Unit 2 reactor which caused the pressure and temperature of the water inside the reactor to climb dramatically.

Although emergency systems came into play and prevented a chain reaction, a relief valve which had opened did not close as the reactor pressure dropped, allowing the coolant to escape. This problem was compounded by the emergency cooling system failing at the same time.

By 6.15 a.m. the reactor core was partially exposed, the reactor building was flooding with the radioactive cooling water and the fuel was radiating through the reactor vessel. The Pennsylvania Emergency Management team were not notified of the incident until 7 a.m. when the situation had become very dangerous.

Although the accident was contained before a major catastrophe occurred, more than 150,000 people evacuated, clean up costs were $1 billion.

WHAT YOU CAN DO

Stop another Three Mile Island. Join the campaign against nuclear power.

USEFUL CONTACTS

Campaign for Nuclear Disarmament (CND)

Friends of the Earth (US)

Greenpeace International

Scottish Campaign to Resist the Atomic Menace

8 The Developing World

The Debt Crisis

LOCATION

Developing Countries – Worldwide

KEY FACTS

Up until 1990 Third World debt was estimated at
$1320 billion, with the biggest individual debtor
Brazil owing $113 billion, followed by Mexico with
$103 billion. Brazil pays back $13 billion annually in
interest payments.

The world's next most indebted countries after
Brazil, are Somalia, Mozambique and Nicaragua
where the national debt is 25 times their foreign
earnings. They are followed by Mexico, Sudan and
Laos who owe 10 times their foreign exchange
earnings. The World Bank considers that owing 2.75
times a country's foreign exchange is a sign of severe
indebtedness. This level of indebtedness is felt by
the poorest members of already poor societies as
education, housing and food are priced beyond
them.

Third World countries are paying so much
interest on their debt that the phenomenon of
reverse aid has appeared. In effect the poorer
countries of the South are paying huge sums of
interest back to the wealthy North helping to boost
the developed countries economies. The
International Monetary Fund (IMF) estimated that
this reverse aid was worth $37 billion in 1985.

As poorer countries are spending huge amounts to service loans they can no longer afford to import, high technology and high cost goods from the wealthier nations. It's estimated that around 6 million jobs in the developed countries have been lost due to lost orders from the indebted nations.

WHAT YOU CAN DO

Write to your bank asking them if they are involved. If so ask them to join the movement to write off or lower interest payments.

CAMPAIGNING ORGANISATIONS

Friends of the Earth (International)

Oxfam

Save the Children

War on Want

Health Care

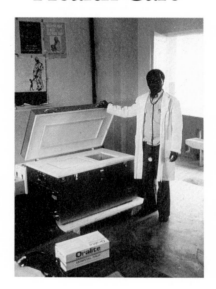

LOCATION

Developing countries – Worldwide

KEY FACTS

Each day about 11,000 children die of diarrhoea in developing countries while almost 15 million die each year of preventable illnesses.

Around the world its now estimated that there are now between six to ten million people infected by HIV; 150,000 babies were born with the infection in sub-saharan Africa during the 1980's.

Each year 5 million people die from malaria while tuberculosis kills another 3 million.

While developed countries have around one doctor for every 500 people, Africa as a whole has one for every 25,000 people. As most African doctors are based in the cities the rate in rural areas can be as high as one to 60,000.

In China the provision of primary health care and a well balanced food distribution system have raised life expectancy to 70 years, well in line with more prosperous societies. While in neighbouring Afghanistan, where a war has been going on for ten years, life expectancy is 41 years.

WHAT YOU CAN DO

The campaigning organisations need your support both in time and money, so they can make the changes.

USEFUL CONTACTS

World Health Organisation

Save the Children

UNICEF

Oxfam

Hunger

LOCATION

Developing countries – Worldwide

KEY FACTS

The world's harvest for 1986 could support 6 billion people, more than the whole planet's population, yet 1 billion people still did not get enough food and around 400 million got less than 80% of their calorific needs.

India's wheat harvest doubled between the mid 1960's and the 1970's, and by 1985 it had a surplus of 24 million tonnes. However, individual consumption didn't rise. In effect the poorest section of society cannot afford to buy the extra food.

In 1984, one quarter of the African population, 140 million people, were fed from imported grain.

The population of the rich northern countries eat 30–40% more than the required calories, while in poorer countries, people eat 10% less than the United Nations recommended 2,400 calories.

One quarter of the food produced in the US is wasted either by rotting or being thrown away, yet around the world 11 million children under the age of five die from hunger or hunger-related illness.

About 40% of the world's grain harvest is used as animal feed, to provide meat for wealthy developed countries.

WHAT YOU CAN DO

Try to eat a little less. Cut down on meat. Press your governments to increase aid to the developing world and support the campaigning organisations.

USEFUL CONTACTS

Oxfam

War on Want

Vegetarian Society

Population

LOCATION

Worldwide

KEY FACTS

Mexico City is the worlds fastest growing city. In 1960 its population was 7 million it's now 15 million and is expected to be 30 million by the year 2000.

Kenya is the fastest growing nation in the world. The population is doubling every 17 years; at the moment it'ss over 23 million; it's expected to be over 79 million by the year 2020.

In India the population is now at 817 million, it will be around 1,309 million by 2020. Attempts at population control have had a very limited success.

The world's most populous country is China with 1,087 million. The one child policy has reduced the annual growth rate to 1.4 but by the year 2020 the population will be 1,414 million.

Over the last 20 years Africa's population has been growing by around 3% per year.

Although falling in some countries, child

mortality rates remain high in most of the Third World. For example, in Ethiopia 26 percent of children will die before they are five years old.

Due to female education and land reforms, the state of Kerala, India has reduced the birthrate to 1.5%, the same as Australia.

WHAT YOU CAN DO

The growing world population affects us all. It can only be controlled through education and economic stability. Press your governments to increase aid to the developing world and support the campaigning organisations.

USEFUL CONTACTS

Oxfam

Save the Children

Red Cross

World Health Organisation

World Education

LOCATION

Worldwide

KEY FACTS

Around the world there are around 850 million people who cannot read and write; more than 100 million children are unable to get a primary education.

The total number of illiterate people in the world has grown by 80 million since 1970 with 46% of the world's women, unable to read or write.

The World Bank estimated that just four years of primary education can increase a farmers productivity by 10%. In the developing world the illiterate members of the population are the poorest fed and the least healthy. Studies have shown that people eat better and are healthier, have less children and have more surviving children when they have had even the most basic education.

One of the effects of the recessions of the 1980's was the impact on Third World education programmes. As economies were squeezed, the education budgets were cut and the number of pupils fell. Prior to this many countries in Africa were spending as much as one-fifth of their nation budgets on education and working towards universal child education.

In many Muslim countries education of women is still a very low priority; in Afghanistan only 8% of the women are literate while in the Yemen the rate is 3%. Saudi Arabia with one of the highest per capita incomes in the world has an adult literacy rate of between 40 and 59% the missing numbers are the women.

WHAT YOU CAN DO

Support the drive to educate the world.

USEFUL CONTACTS

United Nations Education Science and Cultural

Organisation (UNESCO)

Directory of Organisations

Friends of the Earth
(International)
P.O. Box 19199
1000 GD
Amsterdam,
Tel. (20) 622 1369

Argentina – Amigos de la
Tierra
Cassilla Correo 3560
CP 1000
Buenos Aires
Tel. 54 1 771 3670

Australia – Friends of the
Earth
P.O. Box 530
Melbourne 3001
Victoria
Tel. 61 3 4198700

Austria – Freunde der Erde
Mariahilfe Strasse 1052113
1060
Vienna
Tel. 43 222 597 1443

Bangaldesh – Institute for
Environmental and
Development Studies
PO Box 4222
Dhaka 1000
Tel. 880 2 242351

Belgium – Les Amis de la
Terre (Belgium)
Place de la Vingeanne
Dave 5158
Tel. 32 81 401 478

Brazil – ADFG Amigos da
Terra
Rua Miguel Tostes 694
90.000
Porto Alegre
Tel. 55 512 328884

Canada – Les Ami(e)s de la
Terre
251 Laurier Ave W
Suite 701
Ottawa
ON K1P 5J6
Tel. 1 613 230 3352

Cyprus – Friends of the Earth
P.O. Box 3411
Limassol
Tel. 357 43 32139

Denmark – NOAH
Studiesraede 24
DK1455
Copenhagen
Tel. 45 33 156052

Ecuador – Tierra Viva
P.O. Box 1891
Cuena
Tel. 593 7 824621

Estonia – Estonian Green
Movement
ERL
Box 300
202400
Tartu
Tel. 7 0142 3019873517

England and Wales –
Friends of the Earth
26–28 Underwood Street
London
N17 JQ
Tel. 071 490 1555

France – Les Amis de la
  Terre
62 Bis,
Rue des Peupliers
92100
Bologne
Billancourt
Tel. 33 1 491 0457

Ghana – Friends of the
  Earth
P.O. Box 3794
Accra

Indonesia – WALHI
J1 Penjernihan 115
  Kompleks
Keuangan Pejompongan
Jakarta Pusat 10210
Tel. 62 21 588416586820

Ireland – Earthwatch
Harbour View
Bantry
County Cork
Tel. 353 27 50968151283

Italy – Amici della Terra
Via del Sudario,
35 00186
Rome
Tel. 39 6 68753086868289

Japan – Chikyu no Tomo
801 Shibuya Mansions 7–1
Uguisudani-cho Shibuya-ku
Toyoko 150
Tel. 81 3 770 5387

Luxembourg – Mouvement
  Ecologique
6 Rue Vauban
Luxembourg
Tel. 439030

Malaysia – Sahabat Alam
  malaysia
43 Salween Toad
10050
Pulao
Penang
Teł. 60 4 376930375705

Netherlands – Vereniging
  Milieudefensie
Damrak 26 1012 LJ
Amsterdam
Tel. 31 20 221366

Netherlands Antilles –
  Amigu di Tera
P.O. Box 2144
Willemstad
Curacao
Tel. 599 9 73965

New Zealand – Friends of
  the Earth
P.O. Box 39–065
Auckland
Tel. 64 9 34319

Nicaragua – ABEN
Casa Ricardo Morales Aviles
  1c
3 12 al Sur
Managua
Tel. 505 2
  237652444822701

Pakistan – Environmental
  Management Society
371 Shaoib lodge,
Ambajee Villa Road,
Gazdarabad,
Karachi 74200
Tel. 92 21 4466

Papua New Guinea –
  Friends of the Earth
P.O. Box 4028
Boroko
Tel. 675 260 738

Poland – Polski Klub
  Ecologiczney
Miedzynarodowa 3234a
  m167
03 992 Warsaw
Tel. Warsaw 03 922

Portugal – Amigos da Terra
Rua Pinheiro Chagas,
28–2,
Dto. 1000
Lisbon
Tel. 351 1 543615543622

Scotland – Friends of the
Earth
Bonnington Mill
72 Newhaven Road
Edinburgh
EH6 5 QG
Tel. 031 554 9977

Sierra Leone – Friends of
the Earth
P.M. Bag 950 33
Robert Town
Freetown

Spain – Fed. de Amigos de
la Tierra
Av. Betanzos 55,
11.1 28029
Madrid
Tel. 34 1 201 4496

Sweden – Jordens Vanner
Fjallagatan 23A S-116 45
Stockholm
Tel. 46 8 702201718

Switzerland – Freunde der
Erde
Engelstrasse 12a
CH 9000
St Gall
Tel. 41 71 232303

Tanzania – Tanzanian
Environmental Society
P.O. Box 1309
Dar Es Salaam
Tel. 255 51 7407564455

United States – Friends of
the Earth
218 D St. SE
Washington DC 20003
Tel.(202) 544 2600

Uruguay – REDES/ Amigos
de la Tierra
4113cc 15229
Montevideo
Tel. 598 2 381640

West Germany – BUND
Postfach 300220 5300
Bonn 3
Tel. 49 228 4009736

Greenpeace Offices

Greenpeace International
Stichting Greenpeace
Council
Keizersgracht 176
1016 DW Amsterdam

Greenpeace Australia
Main Office
Studio 14, 37 Nicholson
Street
Balmain
NSW 2041

Greenpeace Canada
Main Office
578 Bloor Street West
Toronto
M6G 1K1

Greenpeace New Zealand
Private Bag
Wellesley Street
Auckland

Greenpeace USA
1436 U Street NW
Washington DC
20009

Animal Aid
7 Castle Street
Tonbridge,
Kent
TN9 1BH
Tel. 0732 364546

Animal Concern (Scotland)
62 Old Dumbarton Road
Glasgow
G3 8 RE
Tel 041 334 6014

Animal Liberation Front
Box 19
8 Elm Avenue
Nottingham
NG3 4 GF

Ark Foundation
498–500 Harrow Road
London
W9 3QA
Tel. 071 968 6780

Asia-Pacific People's
Environmental Network
c/o Sahabat Alam Malaysia
43 Salween Toad
10050
Pulao
Penang

Association for the
Conservation of Energy
9 Sherlock Mews,
London
W1M 3 RH
Tel. 071 935 1495

Associaion for the
Protection of Rural
Scotland
14a Napier Road
Edinburgh
EH10 5 AY
Tel. 031 229 1081

The Atlantic Salmon Trust
Ltd
Moulin
Pitlochry
Perthshire
PH16 5 JQ
Tel. 0796 3439

Acid Rain Information
Centre
Department of
Environmental and
Geographical Studies
Manchester Polytechnic
Chester Street
Manchester
M1 5 GD
Tel. 061 228 6171 ex. 2421

Aluminium Can Recycling
Association
Suite 308
I-Mex House
52 Blucher Street
Birmingham
B1 1QU
Tel. 021 633 4656

Animal Aid Society
7 Castle Street
Tonbridge
Kent
TN9 1 BH
Tel. 0732 364546

Animal Vigilantes
24 Salisbury Street
Fordingbridge
Hampshire
SP6 1AF
Tel. 0425 53663

The Antartica Project
624 9th Street NW
Suite 500
Washington
DC 20001
USA

The Bat Conservation Trust
c/o The Conservation
Foundation
Lower Lodge
1 Kensington Gore
London

British Antartic Survey
High Cross
Madingley Road
Cambridge
CB3 0ET

BP Solar
Solar House
36 Bridge Street
Leatherhead
Surrey
Tel. 0372 377899

British Plastic Federation
5 Belgrave Square
London
SW1X 8PD
Tel. 071 235 9483

British Waste Paper
    Association
Alexander House
Station Road
Aldershot
Hants
GU11 1BQ
Tel. 0252 344454

British Glass Manufacturers
    Confederation
Northumberland Road
Sheffield
S10 2 UA
Tel. 0742 686201

British Cycling Federation
(BCF)
36 Rockingham Road
Kettering
Northamptonshire
NN16 8HG
Tel. 0536 412211

Bicycle Association of Great
    Britain
(BAGB)
Starley House
Eaton Road
Coventry
West Midlands

Beauty Without Cruelty
57 King Henry's Walk
London
N1 4NX
Tel. 071 254 2929

Barn Owl Trust
Waterleaf
Ashburton
Devon
TQ 13 7HU
Tel. 0364 53036

British Union for the
    Abolition of Vivisection
16A Crane Grove
Islington
London
N7 8 LB
Tel. 071 700 4888

British Coal
Hobart House
Grosvenor Place
London
SW1X 7AE
Tel. 071 235 2020

Bio-dynamic Agricultural
    Association
Woodman Lane
Clent
Stourbridge
West Midlands
DY9 9 PX
Tel. 0562 884933

British Cycling Federation
36 Rockingham Road
Kettering
Northhamptonshire
NN16 8 HG
Tel. 0563 412211

Bhopal Victims Support
    Committee
5052 Kings Street
Southall
Middlesex

British Ecolocical Society
Burlington House
Piccadilly
London
W1V 0LQ

British Nuclear Fuels Ltd
(BFNL)
Risley
Warrington
Cheshire
WA3 5AS
Tel. 0925 832000

British Plastics Federation
5 Belgrave Square
London
SW1
Tel. 071 235 9483

British Trust for
Conservation Volunteers
36 St Mary's Street
Wallingford
Oxfordshire
OX10 0EU
Tel. 0491 39766

Campaign for Lead Free Air
3 Endsleigh Street
London
WC1H 0DD
Tel. 071 387 4970

Campaign for Nuclear
Disarmament
22–24 Underwood Street
London
N1 7JQ

Can Makers Information
Service
36 Grosvenor Gardens
London
SW1W 0EB
Tel. 071 629 9621

Care for the Wild
1 Ashfolds
Horsham Road
Rusper
Sussex
RH12 4 QX

Centre for Alternative
Technology
Machynlleth
Powys
SY20 9AZ
Tel. 0654 702400

Compassion in World
Farming
(CIWF)
20 Lavant street,
Petersfield
Hampshire
GU32 3EW
Tel. 0730 64208
Tel. 0730 68863

Chickens Lib
P.O. Box 2
Holmfirth
Huddersfield
HD7 1QT
Tel. 0484 683158

Consumers Association
2 Marylebone Road
London
NW1 4 DX
Tel. 071 486 5544

Council for the Protection
of Rural England
(CPRE)
Warwick House
25 Buckingham Palace
Road
London
SW1W 0PP
Tel. 071 976 6433

Cities for People
26–28 Underwood Street
London
N1 7 JQ
Tel. 071 490 1555

The Countryside
  Commission
John Dower House
Crescent Place
Gloucestershire
GL50 3RA
Tel. 0242 521381

Compassion in World
  Farming
20 Lavant Street
Petersheild
Hampshire
GU32 3 EW
Tel. 0730 64208

Coalition Clean Baltic
  (CCB)
Swedish Society for Nature
  Conservation
P.O. Box 4510
S-102 65 Stockholm
Tel. 46 18 46 99 66

Cyclists Association
  (CTC)
Cotterhill House
69 Meadrow
Godalming
Surrey
GU7 3HS
Tel. 0468 7217

Department of Energy
Energy Efficieny Office
Blackhorse Road
London
SE99 6 UB

Earth Island Institute
300 Broadway, Suite 28
San Francisco
CA 94133
Tel. (415) 788 3666

Ecoglassnost
Dondukov 61v.39
Sofia
Bulgaria

Elefriends
Cherry Tree Cottage
Coldharbour
Dorking
Surrey
RH5 6HA
Tel. 0308 713320

Environmental
  Investigation Agency
208–209 Upper Street
London
N1 1RL

Ecover
Full Moon
Steyning
BN4 3DG

Fund for the Replacement
of Animals in Experiments
(FRAME)
Eastgate House
34 Stoney Street
Nottingham
NG1 1NB

Foundation to Protect the
  Hungarian Environment
84 Old North Stamford
  Road
Stamford CT 06905
United States

General Motors AG
P.O. Box
Stelzen Strasse 4
CH-8152 Glattbrugg
Zurich
Switzerland

Glasgow for People
420 Sauchiehall Street
Glasgow
G2 3JD

Green Deserts
Geoff's House,
Rougham
Bury St Edmunds,
Suffolk
IP30 9LY
Tel. 0359 70265

Green Alliance
(GA)
60 Chandos Place
London
WC2N 4 HG
Tel. 071 836 0341

Healthy Cities
Environmental Health
Dept.
Glasgow District Council
City Chambers
George Square
Glasgow
Tel. 041 221 9600

Henry Doubleday Research
Association
(HDRA)
Nation Centre for Organic
Gardening
Ryton-on-Dunsmorre
Coventry
CV8 3LG

The Hawk Trust
c/o Birds of Prey Section
Zoological Society of
London
Regents Park
London

International Board for
Plant Genetic Resources
c/o FOA United Nations
via Delle Sette Chiese 142
00145
Rome
Tel. 39 (6) 5744719

International Council for
Bird Preservation
32 Cambridge Road
Girton
Cambridge
CB3 0PJ
Tel. 0223 277318

Intermediate Technology
Development Group
(ITDG)
Myson House
Railway Terrace
Rugby
CV21 3HT
Tel. 0788 60631

International Rivers
Network
301 Broadway, Suite B
San Franvcisco
California
Tel. (415) 986 4694 Fax
(415) 398 2732

International Whaling
Commission
(IWC)
Red House
Station Road
Histon
Cambridge
CB4 4NP
Tel. 0223 233971

Institute for Waste
Management
3 Albion Place
Derngate
Northampton
NN1 1UD
Tel. 0604 20426

IWW-Earth First!
106 Standley Street
Ukiah
CA 95482
Tel. (707) 468 10660

International Work Group
    for Indigenous Affairs
(IWGIA)
Fiolstraede 10,
DK-1171
Copenhagan K
Denmark

Italian League for the
    Protection of Birds
(LIPU UK)
6 Butlers Close
Broomfield
Chelmsford
Essex
CM1 5 BE
Tel. 0245 440567

Lothian and Edinburgh
    Environmental
    Partnership
Bonnington Mill
72 Newhaven Road
Edinburgh
EH6 5 QG
Tel. 031 557 6628

The Lothian Bat Group
Natural History
    Department
Nation Museums of
    Scotland
Chambers Street
Edinburgh
EH1 1JF

LYNX
P.O. Box 916
Dunmow
Essex
CM6 1UH
Tel. 0371 2016

League Against Cruel
    Sports
Sparling House
83–87 Union Street
London SE1 1SG
Tel. 071 407 0979

Marine Conservation
    Society
9 Gloucester Road
Ross-on-Wye
Herefordshire
HR9 5BU
Tel. 0989 66017

Mountaineering Council
    for Scotland
4e Battery Terrace
Oban
Argyll
PA34 5DN
Tel. 0631 62244

Moeen Qureshi,
Senior Vice President for
    Operation
The World Bank
1818 H Street
NW
Washington, DC
20433

Minister of State for the
    Environment and Forests
Paryavaran Bhawan
CGO Complex
Lodi Road
New Delhi
110019
India

National Audobon Society
801 Pennsylvania Avenue
    SE
Washington DC
2003
Tel. (202) 5479009

Nature Conservancy
    Council
(NCC)
Northminster House
Peterborough
PE1 1UA
Tel. 0733 40345

National Society for Clean
  Air
(NSCA)
136 North Street
Brighton
BN1 1RG
Tel. 0273 26313

Oxfam
274 Banbury Road
Summertown
Oxford
OX2 7 DZ

Parents for Safe Food
Britannia House
1–11 Glenthorne Road
London
W6 0LT

Pesticide Trust
23 Beehive Place
London SW9 7QR
071 274 8895

President Suharto
President RI
Insta Negra
Jalan Vetreran
Jakarta
Indonesia

Rainforest Action Network
310 Broadway
San Franscisco
California 94133
Tel. (415) 3984404

Royal Society for the
  Protection of Birds
The Lodge
Sandy
Bedfordshire
SG19 2 DL

Royal Society for the
  Prevention of Cruelty to
  Animals
The Causeway
Horsham
Sussex
RH12 1HG
Tel. 0403 64181

Royal Society for Nature
  Conservation
(RSNC)
The Green
Nettleham
Lincoln
LN2 2NR
Tel. 0522 752326

Save the Children Fund
Mary Datchelor House
17 Grove Lane
London SE5

The Sea Turtle Protection
  Society of Greece
(STPS)
P.O. Box 51154
Kifisia
14510
Greece

Scottish Wildlife Trust
25 Johnstone Terrace
Edinburgh
EH1
Tel. 031 226 4602

Swedish Environmental
  Protection Agency
S171 85
Solna
Sweden
Tel. 46 8 799 1000 Fax 46 8
  28 3361

Scottish Wildlife and
 Countryside Link
Southesk Bank
St Magdalene's Lane
Perth
PH2 0 BW
Tel. 0738 30804

Save the Cairngorms
 Campaign
P.O. Box 39
Inverness
IV1 2RL

SZOPK
Gorkeho 6
81101 Bratislava
Czechoslovakia

The Sierra Club
408 C Street NE
Washington DC
20002
Tel. (202) 547 6009

Sea Shepherd
P.O. Box 5
Ashford
Middlesex
Tel. 0784 254846

Society for the Prevention
 of Asbestosis and
 Industrial Diseases
38 Drapers Road
Enfield
Middlesex
EN2 8LU

Survival International UK
310 Edgware Road
London
W2 1DY
Tel. 071 723 5535

Survival International US
2121 Decatur Place NW
Washington DC 20008
Tel. (202) 265 1077

Scottish Campaign to Resist
 the Atomic Menace
11 Forth Street
Edinburgh
EH1 3LE
Tel. 031 557 4283
Tel. 031 557 4284

Scottish Salmon Board
Drummond House
Scott Street
Perth
PH1 5 EJ
Tel. 0738 35973

Solar Electric
175 Cascade Court
Rohnert Park
CA 94928
Tel. (707) 586 0690

The Soil Association
86–88 Colston Street
Bristol
BS1 5BB
Tel. 0272 290661

Swedish Society for Nature
 Conservation
P.O. Box 4510
S-102 65 Stockholm
Tel. 46 18 46 99 66

Transport 2000
Walkden House
10 Melton Street
London
NW1 2 EJ
Tel. 071 388 8386

United Glass Ltd
Porters Wood
St Albans
Herfordshire
AL3 6 NY
Tel. 0727 59261

United Nations Education,
    Science and Cultural
    Organisation
(UNESCO)
7 Place de Fontenay
75700
Paris

United Nations Childrens
    Fund
(UNICEF)
Palais de Nations
CH-1211
Geneva
Switzerland

VAK
Kalnciema 30
226406 Riga
Latvia SSR
USSR

The Vegan Society
33–35 George Street
Oxford
OX1 2AY

The Vegetarian Society
Dunham Road
Altringham
Cheshire
WA14 4QG

Whale and Dolphin
    Conservation Society
(WDCS)
20 West Lea Road
Bath
Avon
BA1 3RL
Tel. 0225 334511

Werkgroep Nordzee
    Foundation
vossinsstraat 20–11
1071 AD
Amsterdam

The White Elephant Trust
    (WET)
Albermarle Street
London
W1

World Wide Fund for
    Nature (Austria)
Ottakringerstrasse
114–1169m Oistfacgk 1162
Vienna
Austria

World Wide Fund for
    Nature (GB)
Weyside Park
Godalming
Surrey
GU7 1XR
Tel. 0483 426444

World Health Organisation
Avenue Appia
CH-1211 Geneva 27
Switzerland

War on Want
37–39 Great Guilford
    Street,
London
SE1 0ES

Waste Watch
26 Bedford Square
London
WC1B 3HU
Tel. 071 636 4066

Womens Environmental
    Network
(WEN)
287 City Road
London
EC1V 1LA

Bibliography

Jonathan Porritt – *Where on Earth are we Going* – BBC 1990

James Wilkinson – *Green or Bust* – BBC 1990

Geoffrey Lean, Don Hinrichsen, Adam Markham – *Atlas of the Environment* – Arrow Books 1990

Bill McKibben – *The End of Nature* – Penguin 1990

ed. Norman Myers – *The Gaia Atlas of Planet Management* – Pan Books 1985

ed. Dr Frank Barnaby – *The Gaia Peace Atlas* – Pan Books 1988

ed. D Pearce – *Blueprint for a Green Economy* – Earthscan

John Elkington and Julia Hailes – *The Green Consumer Guide* – Victor Gollancz 1988

Alison Costello, Bernadette Vallely, Josa Young – *The Sanitary Protection Scandal* – Women's Environmental Network 1989

Steve Elsworth – *A Dictionary of the Environment* – Paladin 1990

Department of the Environment – *Our Common Inheritance* – HMSO 1990

The Environment Council – *Who's Who in the Environment, Scotland: England* – The Countryside Commission 1989

Dr Anne Scott – *The Good Beach Guide* – Marine Conservation Society 1989

Alan B Dunning – *Worldwatch Paper 92 Poverty and the Environment: Reversing the Downward Spiral* – Worldwatch Institute 1989

The Bhopal Tragedy – *One Year After* – Appen 1986

Maurice Hansen – *E for Additives* – Thorsons 1985

I have also used many reports and campaign material produced by the campaigning organisations mentioned in the Green Almanac as well as journals and newspapers such New Scientist and the Guardian.